Weather

*Written by David Houghton for
the Royal Yachting Association*

*First published 1968 and
revised annually.*
This edition revised March 2003

An RYA publication

The information contained in this book is
always liable to change but was accurate at
the time of going to press. Any changes will
be notified in Admiralty Notices to Mariners
and similar sources of information.

Published by
The Royal Yachting Association
RYA House Ensign Way Hamble
Southampton SO31 4YA
Tel: 0845 345 0400
Fax: 0845 345 0329
Email: info@rya.org.uk
Web: www.rya.org.uk

CONTENTS

Sources and content of forecasts plus maps and tables

Sea area boundaries

International weather vocabulary

YOUR WEATHER FORECAST

Whether sailing, cruising or merely pottering about close inshore there is nothing more important than the weather. Careful attention to the weather forecast can make all the difference between an enjoyable cruise and an expensive salvage claim, between winning and losing a race, between a fast exhilarating beat across the Channel and a long and tedious one, and between a relaxing afternoon afloat and the depressing moans of a wet, bedraggled and half-frozen crew.

It is just as important to follow the weather as it is to know the tides, and intelligent following of the weather and the weather forecasts can increase enormously one's interest and enjoyment in a cruise or an afternoon's sailing.

Merely listening to a weather forecast is not enough. Listening habits are such that most people use only half an ear and do not remember the details of the forecast. It is essential to write it down on a note-pad, or on one of the specially designed forms which are available for use with the BBC Shipping Forecast. The majority of weather bulletins are transmitted at normal reading speed, but even so, using a prepared form and simple abbreviations all the information can be taken down. Having got it on paper you can think about it at your leisure and plan your day to make the best possible use of the winds and weather which are expected.

This book gives basic guidance on the content and terminology of weather forecasts to enable boaters to understand and collate the information which is given. It also contains details of telephone and fax marine weather services, and weather broadcasts for British home waters and for most of the coastal areas around Europe including the Mediterranean. These details are liable to change but it is hoped that most will remain valid until the next edition is produced.

Every wind forecast needs a certain amount of interpretation and application, especially if you are near to land. Information on pages 22 to 24 provide some basic guidance on the effects of coasts and islands on the wind, effects which are not normally covered in marine forecasts which apply to the open sea.

A more comprehensive and detailed discussion of the weather as it affects sailors is to be found in *Weather at Sea Third Edition 1998*, by David Houghton published by Fernhurst Books, available from the RYA price £12.95 plus 50p postage.

Times and frequencies

In addition to weather bulletins broadcast by national radio services such as the BBC, many coastguard and coast radio stations give weather bulletins at fixed times during the day for sea areas local to the station. Together they cover all sea areas around the coast of Western Europe. These bulletins are broadcast on the VHF (156-174MHz) and MF (1500-3500kHz) maritime bands and may be received on all marine radio-telephone equipment and on some portable receivers.

The tables on page 39 give times of broadcast in GMT. You will often have to add 1 or 2 hours to the times shown when planning to pick up broadcasts.

Frequencies shown as kHz may be converted into metres by doing the simple sum shown on page 39. A formula for conversion from metres per second to knots is also given. A few countries use these units for wind speed instead of knots.

GMDSS - INMARSAT-C

The Global Maritime Distress and Safety System (GMDSS), of which NAVTEX is an integral part, provides for the worldwide automatic receipt on board of navigational and weather information in English transmitted by satellite (Inmarsat) via Standard-C. GMDSS also encompasses radio, telex and telephony broadcasts for coastal waters. It is already operational in the North Atlantic/European sector (METAREAs I, II and III). Warnings and forecasts for METAREA I, the northeast Atlantic north of 48° 27'N, provided by Bracknell are broadcast from the BT Inmarsat station at Goonhilly. METAREA II covering the northeast Atlantic south of 48° 27'N, and METAREA III, the Mediterranean, are the responsibility of the French and Spanish Met Services respectively. Sea areas used in the broadcast from Corsen for METAREA II are shown on page 54. The times of the main weather bulletins, all of them in English, for the areas are:-

METAREA I   – 0930 and 2030 GMT

METAREA II – 0900 and 2100 GMT

METAREA III – 1000 and 2200 GMT

For more detailed information see page 38.

Navtex

Navtex is an international navigational telex service broadcasting safety related messages in English on 518kHz. Dedicated receiving equipment is readily available and not expensive. The simplest version comprises a receiver tuned to the frequency, a small printer and a chip which controls what is received and printed. All messages are prefixed by a 4-character 'word'. The first character identifies the transmitting station, the second the category of message and the remainder are two serial numbers. Details will be found on page 37. This facility to receive gale warnings and marine weather forecasts automatically is particularly valuable for anyone cruising offshore. Twice daily bulletins cover all sea areas around UK and Western Europe.

In UK waters, a 490kHz service broadcasts inshore waters forcasts with a three day outlook, twice a day.

Radio-facsimile

Weather maps, both actual and forecast, and pictures from weather satellites are broadcast according to fixed schedules by a number of national meteorological services. Some of the 'actual' weather charts also include weather observations from selected meteorological stations presented in the standard international code. They are intended mainly for professional use, but they will benefit anyone able to read a weather map. Information on the most useful fax broadcasts is shown on page 36. For how to read the wind from a weather map see page 21.

Volmet

Volmet is a meteorological service for aviators available on HF (SSB mode), and on VHF in southern England and parts of Scotland. The VHF broadcasts are continuous, but the RAF Volmet on HF is now transmitted in five 6-minute slots commencing on the hour, the cycle repeating every half-an-hour. There is no carrier when there is no information being transmitted. Sailors keenly interested in the weather will find the information interesting and in some instances useful. Details of frequencies are given on page 41.

Internet

There is a wealth of useful weather information available on the Internet, including actual and forecast weather charts and hourly weather reports from buoys and lightships around Britain. This information is particularly valuable when planning a passage, and is a good way of keeping in touch with the weather when ashore. See page 25 for a selection of useful sites.

WEATHER INFORMATION AND FORECASTS AVAILABLE IN THE UK

By far the most popular and widely used forecasts for sea areas of northwest Europe are the Shipping Forecasts broadcast by the BBC on Radio 4. French, German and Spanish fishermen swear by them. The script is written in the Met Office's National Meteorological Centre. All forecasts broadcast by the Coastguard also originate from the NMC, as do all gale warnings for UK sea areas. Many of the following basic services are available free within the context of the requirements of the Safety of Life at Sea (SOLAS) Convention and are provided by the Met Office in association with the MCA. However, the Met Office also offers many additional services via telephone, fax and the Internet providing, for a modest fee, more detailed and site specific information.

SHIPPING FORECASTS

Shipping forecasts are broadcast on Radio 4 Long Wave (1515 metres, 198kHz) at 0048, 0536, 1201 and 1754 daily; and on Radio 4 VHF at 0048 and 0536 daily. These are clock times.

Gale warnings are part of the shipping forecast service and are broadcast at the earliest juncture in the Radio 4 programme after receipt from the Met Office, and also after the next following news bulletin.

Each Shipping Forecast Bulletin comprises several parts:

General synopsis

This is very important because it gives the information you need to estimate the time of occurrence of any changes which are forecast for individual sea areas. It tells you about depressions, anticyclones, troughs and fronts which will control the winds and weather over the sea areas in the forecast period. It tells you where they were just before the broadcast was written, which way they are moving and where they are expected to be at the end of the forecast period. Careful interpolation on the basis of the General Synopsis will often double the amount of information you can get from the sea area forecast which follows. The meanings of terms which are used are given on page 15.

Sea area forecast

For each sea area or group of areas around the British Isles a forecast is given of wind, weather and visibility for the following 24 hours. The areas are given in fixed sequence and to save time the words wind, force, weather, visibility are omitted. The meanings of the terms used are given on pages 11 through 17.

Reports from coastal stations

The 0048 and 0536 bulletins end with a list of weather reports from coastal stations around the British Isles. These give the reported wind direction and force, significant weather if any (if the weather is fair or fine nothing is said), visibility in miles or metres, barometric pressure in millibars and the barometric tendency (i.e., whether rising, falling or steady). These reports are very useful because not only do they tell you what the weather is nearest to you but they give you enough detail with the General Synopsis to enable you to construct your own weather map. Do not forget though, if you use them to draw a weather map, the coastal reports are always for a later time than the 'main chart time' (0001, 0600, 1200, 1800 GMT) for which the positions of depressions, troughs etc. are given in the General Synopsis. If you are constructing your own weather map, and you should do it for the time of the coastal station reports, you will need to move on the troughs, and fronts, etc., and adjust the positions given in the General Synopsis to the time of the coastal reports, using the speeds given in the General Synopsis.

Increasingly, manned weather reporting stations are being replaced by automatic ones, and it is important to be aware of their limitations. Automatic stations are not yet capable of reporting 'weather', ie whether it is raining, snowing etc; or of measuring visibility in excess of five miles. So if the visibility is reported as five miles, it does not necessarily mean that it is only five miles. Even more importantly, if the visibility is reported as, say, 500 metres, you have to judge whether the low value is due to fog, rain or snow.

INSHORE WATERS FORECASTS

Forecasts for inshore waters (up to 12 miles offshore) around Britain are broadcast at 0053 and 0540 clock time on BBC Radio 4 (198kHz, 1515m) and VHF, and include at 0053 the most recent available actual weather reports from a selection of coastal stations whose locations are given on page 27.

LAND AREA FORECASTS

These are important because:

a) They include an outlook beyond the period of the detailed forecast and the shipping forecast. On a fairly recent occasion stormy weather was predicted in the weekend outlook at the end of a Friday lunchtime forecast. This was not mentioned in the shipping forecast since the change was not due until well after the end of the period covered by the shipping forecast, but sailors who took action on the land area forecast saved themselves a lot of trouble and inconvenience, while some who did not heed the forecasts were shipwrecked and taken ashore by the rescue services.

b) They may give details about coastal weather for which there is not space in the shipping bulletin.

FORECASTS AND REPORTS ON LOCAL RADIO

All local radio stations near the coast, broadcast weather forecasts for the local area and many of them include information on winds and weather over the nearby coastal waters, particularly during the summer months. Since the time and content of the various broadcasts are frequently adjusted the detailed information is not included in this book. However, you will find that the best times to tune into your local radio station for a weather bulletin are between 30 and 35 minutes past 0600, 0700 and 0800 and/or sometime between 0650 and 0715, and again between 0750 and 0815, and between 1700 and 1830.

FORECASTS AND REPORTS BY TELEPHONE, FAX AND THE INTERNET

Forecasts and up-to-date weather reports are readily available for a fee by telephone, fax and the Internet for all coasts, coastal and inland waters of the UK and the Western Mediterranean. The services, specially designed for sailors are provided by the Met Office. Details are given on pages 25 and 29 to 33.

Marinecall

The Marinecall (telephone) service provides on separate numbers:

- 2-day forecasts for coastal waters of the UK in 16 separate areas. Each forecast comprises any gale and strong wind warnings in force, a General Synopsis, a forecast of wind, weather, visibility, air temperature, sea state and sea temperature for the next 24 hours and an outlook for the following 24 hours.
- The latest available hourly weather reports for stations in each area.
- 2 to 5-day planning forecasts for the UK and The English Channel.

MetFAX

The MetFAX Marine service provides on separate numbers:

- 2-day forecasts for all coastal waters of the UK in 16 separate areas – as provided on the Marinecall telephone service - plus the latest actual and forecast (24 hour) weather maps.

- 2 to 5-day planning forecasts for six areas stretching from Faeroes in the north to Fitzroy in the south.
- the latest actual and forecast weather maps (without written forecasts attached).
- a chart of the latest weather reports from some 60 stations over the British Isles and adjacent European coasts. The reports are plotted in standard format - a key is included - giving details of wind, pressure, temperature, cloud and weather. The chart can be accessed approximately 30 minutes after the time of the reports and is updated every three hours. You can easily use it to construct your own weather map, drawing the isobars from the pressure readings, and so follow weather changes throughout the day in considerable detail.
- the latest shipping forecast as broadcast on Radio 4.
- the latest picture from the weather satellite.

Weathercall

Weathercall is essentially a landsman's forecast, but you will need it for sailing on inland waters.

Similar fax services are provided for pilots on **MetFAX Aviation** and for schools on MetFAX Education. You may find some of these products of interest. For instance, the MetFAX Education menu includes plotted weather reports for the east coast of the USA. Dialling codes for all the index pages will be found on page 34.

Marine Mobile Services

The following services are available on any mobile network via SMS or WAP.

Time and Place Forecasts(TPF)

Forecasts for the next six hours, updated hourly for more than 2,500 areas, each of three square miles.

Inshore Waters Forecasts

Forecasts for the next 24 hours for UK inshore waters out to 12 miles offshore; updated twice daily at 0500 and 2300.

Shipping Areas Forecasts

An abbreviated version of the latest BBC broadcast covering 30 sea areas and updated four times daily (0001, 0500, 1100 and 1700).

Coastal Station Reports

The actual conditions at 48 coastal stations. Updated hourly, with some every 3 hours.

To set up and use these services go to www.metoffice.com and click on Mobile Services. Details of the menu and command codes are on page 29 to 32.

FORECASTS VIA THE COASTGUARD

Coastguard Marine Rescue Co-ordination Centres (MRCCs) and Sub-Centres (MRSCs) (listed on page 31) provide a comprehensive schedule which includes the broadcast of Gale Warnings, Strong Wind Warnings, those parts of the Shipping forecast relevant to the area served by the particular CG station and an Inshore Waters forecast. Details are on page 28.

WARNING SERVICES

Gale warnings form an important part of the weather services provided by national and coastal radio stations and via Navtex. Always remember however that warnings are issued mostly for winds of gale force (34 knots) and above because at this strength the wind becomes a hazard for commercial shipping and trawling. The 'yachtsman's gale' is more like Force 6 (22 to 27 knots) while for many small sailing and motor boats Force 4 (11 to 16 knots) is the limit of safety.

A strong wind warning service operates for the benefit of small craft in the coastal waters of Britain. These warnings are disseminated via the Coastguard MRCCs and MRSCs (on receipt and at four-hourly intervals thereafter). Many BBC and independent local radio stations on or near the coast have also agreed to broadcast these warnings.

Warnings are issued whenever winds of Force 6 or above are expected over the coastal strip (waters up to 5 miles offshore). The warnings cover the period up to 12 hours ahead and whenever possible advance warning of up to six hours is given. A warning is also issued if there is a Gale Warning in force for the sea area even though the winds are not expected to reach Force 6 in the coastal strip. The warning will then state that winds are not expected to reach Force 6 in the coastal strip, but that there is a warning of gales to seaward. Note that strong wind warnings automatically expire 12 hours after issue.

FORECAST FOR FISHING FLEETS

Three-day forecasts, primarily for the benefit of the fishing fleets in the North Sea and South Western Approaches, are broadcast by Aberdeen, Humber and Falmouth Coastguard stations from 1 October until 31 March. An initial announcement is made on 2182kHz and the broadcast is on 2226kHz. The forecasts for Viking, Cromarty, Forth, Forties, Fisher and Fair Isle are broadcast by Aberdeen at 2020 and repeated the next morning at 0820. Tyne, Dogger, German Bight, Humber and Thames, by Humber at 2110 and repeated the next morning at 0910. Plymouth, Fastnet, Shannon, Sole, Finisterre by Falmouth at 2150 and repeated the next morning at 0950.

TELEVISION AND TELETEXT
WEATHER FORECASTS

Most BBC and ITV channels give regular coverage around news times and near close down. The chart shown is usually the latest actual chart, but in some of the longer presentations a forecast chart is also included. Both Ceefax and Oracle services include weather information and forecasts. Go to Ceefax page 409 or Teletext page 108 for inshore waters forecast.

SPECIAL FORECAST SERVICES

'Talk to a forecaster' is an interactive fax or phone service from the Met Office accessible from anywhere in the world, and includes the opportunity to consult a forecaster or receive fax forecasts abroad. Payment is online by credit card - see page 33.

Clubs may, for a fee, make arrangements for the provision of special forecasts and warnings for particular sailing events. MetFAX Marine can be a very useful part of such a service.

The Met Office now operates a 24 x 7 customer centre for all enquiries. The number is 0845 300 0 300 Fax 0845 300 1 300

The following special Marinecall Services are available to RYA members:

MarineClub - a prepaid service providing discounted 5-day forecasts by telephone.
FaxDirect - providing discounted forecasts faxed automatically on a daily or weekly basis.
E-Marinecall - providing pre-selected forecasts by email.

For more information on these services telephone 0870 600 4219

For long offshore passages weather routeing services are available from Ocean Routes or Noble Denton - see page 34.

INTERNET - ON LINE WEATHER INFORMATION

See pages 25 - 26 for the most useful sites.

MetWEB

MetWEB is a range of comprehensive and up-to-date Met Office weather products online. For occasional use or regular access, MetWEB is a flexible and efficient way to get weather data.

How it Works

- MetWEB is highly flexible, and suitable for both regular and occasional users
- MetWEB uses a prepaid 'ticket' system following telephone registration
- £10 puts 20 tickets in your personal MetWEB account
- Each individual product costs between one and three tickets
- You can top-up online, anytime, anywhere

Setting up your MetWEB account is fast and simple - call 0845 300 0300 or +44 1344 855 680 if outside the UK. This call centre is manned 24 hours a day. VISA, MasterCard, Delta and Switch all accepted. Customers buying tickets to the value of £100 or more can be invoiced on request.

Products available are:

- Surface pressure charts
- 2 day inshore forecasts
- 3 to 5 day inshore outlooks
- 2 to 5 day planning
- Satellite pictures
- Shipping forecasts
- Gale warnings
- Coastal reports
- Western Mediterranean (5 day forecasts for the five areas)
- Weather reports

TERMS USED IN WEATHER FORECASTS AND THEIR MEANINGS

Gale warnings

Warnings are issued for:

Gale

If the mean wind is expected to increase to Force 8 (34 knots) or over, or gusts of 43 knots or over are expected. Gusts as high as 43 knots may occur with the mean wind below 34 knots in cold, unstable and showery airstreams.

Severe gale

If the mean wind is expected to increase to Force 9 (41 knots) or over, or gusts of 52 knots or over are expected.

Storm

If the mean wind is expected to increase to Force 10 (48 knots) or over, or gusts of 61 knots or over are expected.

Winds above Force 10 can only be of academic interest to yachtsmen and will not be detailed here.

The words imminent, soon and later have precise meanings as follows:

Imminent – within 6 hours of issue of the warning.
Soon – 6 to 12 hours from time of issue.
Later – beyond 12 hours from time of issue.

Wind

The wind direction is always the direction from which the wind is blowing: Veer means a clockwise change in wind direction, e.g. from west to northwest: Back means an anticlockwise change in direction, e.g. from northwest to west.

In sea area forecasts wind strengths are always given in terms of the Beaufort Force.

Gusts

The Beaufort Scale of wind force categorises the mean, or average wind. For winds of gale force and above, the strength of gusts is also included at a value approximately 25% stronger than the mean wind. However, gusts must be expected at all wind speeds especially in cold unstable airstreams when 25% over the mean must be regarded as the norm.

BEAUFORT SCALE OF WIND FORCE

Beaufort number	General Description	Sea Criterion	Landsman Criterion	Limits of velocity in knots
0	Calm	Sea like a mirror	Calm; smoke rises vertically.	Less than 1
1	Light air	Ripples with the appearance of scales are formed, but without foam crests.	Direction of wind shown by smoke drift but not by wind vanes.	1 to 3
2	Light breeze	Small wavelets, still short but more pronounced. Crests have a glassy appearance and do not break.	Wind felt on face; leaves rustle; ordinary vane moved by wind.	4 to 6
3	Gentle breeze	Large wavelets. Crests begin to break. Foam of glassy appearance. Perhaps scattered white horses.	Leaves and small twigs in constant motion. Wind extends light flags.	7 to 10
4	Moderate breeze	Small waves becoming longer, fairly frequent white horses.	Raises dust and loose paper; small branches are moved.	11 to 16
5	Fresh breeze	Moderate waves, taking more pronounced long form; many white horses are formed. Chance of some spray.	Small trees in leaf begin to sway. Crested wavelets form on inland waters.	17 to 21
6	Strong breeze	Large waves begin to form; the white foam crests are more extensive everywhere. Probably some spray.	Large branches in motion; whistling heard in telegraph wires, umbrellas used with difficulty.	22 to 27
7	Near gale	Sea heaps up and white foam from breaking waves begins to be blown in streaks along the direction of the wind.	Whole trees in motion; inconvenience felt when walking against wind.	28 to 33
8	Gale	Moderately high waves of greater length; edges of crests begin to break into spindrift. The foam is blown in well-marked streaks along the direction of the wind.	Breaks twigs off trees; generally impedes progress.	34 to 40

9	Severe gale	High waves. Dense streaks of foam along the direction of the wind. Crests of waves begin to topple, tumble and roll over. Spray may affect visibility.	Slight structural damage occurs (chimney-pots and slates removed).	41 to 47
10	Storm	Very high waves with long overhanging crests. The resulting foam in great patches is blown in dense white streaks along the direction of the wind. On the whole the surface takes on a white appearance. The tumbling of the sea becomes very heavy and shock-like. Visibility affected.	Seldom experienced inland; trees uprooted; considerable structural damage occurs.	48 to 55
11	Violent storm	Exceptionally high waves. The sea is completely covered with long white patches of foam lying along the direction of the wind. Everywhere the edges of the wave crests are blown into froth. Visibility affected.		56 to 63
12	Hurricane	Air filled with foam and spray. Sea completely white with driving spray. Visibility very seriously affected.		Greater than 63

FRENCH BEAUFORT SCALE OF WIND FORCE

Degrés	Termes descriptif	Vitesse moyenne en noeuds	Vitesse moyenne en km/h	Aspect de la mer dont on déduit
0	Calme	inf. à 1	inf. à 1	Comme un miroir
1	Très légère brise	1 - 3	1 - 5	Quelques rides
2	Légère brise	4 - 6	6 - 11	Vaguelettes ne déferiant pas
3	Petite brise	7 - 10	12 - 19	Les moutons apparaissent
4	Jolie brise	11 - 16	20 - 28	Petites vagues, nombreux moutons
5	Bonne brise	17 - 21	29 - 38	Vagues modérées, moutons, embruns
6	Vent frais	22 - 27	39 - 49	Lames, crêtes d'écume blanche, embruns
7	Grand frais	28 - 33	50 - 61	Lames déferiantes, trâinés d'écume

8	Coup de vent	34 - 40	62 - 74	Tourbilions d'écume à la crête des lames, traînées d'écume
9	Fort coup de vent	41 - 47	75 - 88	Lames défereantes, grosses à énormes,visibilité réduite par les embruns
10	Tempête	48 - 55	89 - 102	Lames défereantes, grosses à énormes, visibilité réduite par les embruns
11	Violente tempête	56 - 63	103 - 117	Lames défereantes, grosses à énormes, visibilité réduite par les embruns
12	Ouragan	64	118	Lames défereantes, grosses à énormes, et plus et plus visibilité réduite par les embruns

Les vitesses se rapportent au vent moyen et non aux rafales.

DESCRIPTIVE TERMS USED IN LAND AREA FORECASTS

In land area forecasts winds are always given in terms of moderate, fresh, etc. and these terms are defined as follows:

Beaufort Force

Calm	0
Light	1-3
Moderate	4
Fresh	5
Strong	6-7
Gale	8

'Brisk' is occasionally used in place of 'Fresh'

VISIBILITY

In sea area forecasts, visibility descriptions have the following meanings:

Good	More than 5 nautical miles
Moderate	2 to 5 nautical miles
Poor	1,000 metres to 2 nautical miles
Fog	Less than 1,000 metres

In land area reports and forecasts fog is defined as:

Fog	Visibility 200 to 1,000 metres
Thick Fog	Visibility less than 200 metres
Dense Fog	Visibility less than 50 metres

In coastal station reports and aviation forecasts the definitions are:

Mist or Haze	Visibility 1,000 to 2,000 metres
Fog	Visibility less than 1,000 metres

WEATHER

This is not included in reports from automatic stations.

The terms rain, snow, hail etc are obvious enough but the use of the word **fair** calls for some definition. The weather is described as fair when there is nothing significant i.e. no rain, fog, showers, etc. It may or may not be cloudy.

PRESSURE AND PRESSURE TENDENCY

The General Synopsis often gives the values of the pressure at the centres of important weather systems, while the coastal station reports give recorded atmospheric pressure at a selection of stations and the pressure tendency. The millibar is the unit used for pressure in shipping bulletins and on most charts published in the press and elsewhere. Some countries have replaced millibar by hectopascal as the name for the standard unit of pressure. There is no numerical difference between the two.

One millibar (or mb) = one hectopascal (or hPa)

The terms used for pressure tendency in the coastal station reports are defined as follows:

Steady	Change less than 0.1mb in 3 hours
Rising slowly or falling slowly	Change 0.1 to 1.5mb in last 3 hours
Rising or falling	Change 1.6 to 3.5mb in last 3 hours
Rising quickly or falling quickly	Change 3.6 to 6.0mb in last 3 hours
Rising or falling very rapidly	Change of more than 6.0mb in last 3 hours
Now falling, now rising	Change from rising to falling or vice versa within last 3 hours

BEWARE of reading too much into reports of rising slowly, falling slowly, now falling and now rising if general pressure changes are small. Every day there are small ups and downs in pressure all over the world due to the atmospheric tide. In the south of the UK the tidal pressure variation is just under 1 mb. At the equator it is 3mb. The highest values of pressure due to this tide are at 1000 and 2200, the lowest at 0400 and 1600: the same local times everywhere in the world. So if at 0400 and 1600 the pressure is reported as falling slowly it does not mean the weather is likely to or beginning to deteriorate. Similarly if at 1000 and 2200 the pressure is reported as rising slowly it says nothing about improvement.

THE GENERAL SYNOPSIS AND PREAMBLE TO LAND AREA FORECASTS

Depressions

A **depression** is synonymous with a **low** (i.e. low pressure system with a central vortex) or a cyclone (but only the relatively weak tropical cyclones are called depressions). A depression is a cyclonic vortex in the atmosphere in which the winds circulate anticlockwise in the northern hemisphere (clockwise in the southern hemisphere), and blow slightly inwards towards the centre. Depressions in middle latitudes vary enormously in size and energy. Their diameter may be anything from 100 to 2,000 miles with winds of from about 10 to over 70 knots at the surface and central pressure from below 950 millibars in a really deep depression to perhaps as high as 1,025 millibars in a very shallow one. Their speed of movement may be anything up to 60 knots. In a newly formed depression the circular spiralling motion of the air may extend upwards to only a thousand metres or so at most, while in an old depression it may extend upwards to over 15,000 metres.

A **deepening** depression is one in which the central pressure is falling, and in which the winds and rain must be expected to increase. In a **filling** depression the reverse applies. A **vigorous** depression may be large or small but is characterised by strong winds and a lot of rain. A **complex** depression has more than one centre of low pressure.

The simplest form of depression is a perfectly circular system in which the winds are the same speed all the way round and decrease gradually as you move out from the centre. The nearest approach to this ideal is found in the tropics, but in middle latitude, their shape and wind distribution vary greatly. In some, the strongest winds are near the centre, in others the strongest winds may be 500 miles out from the centre.

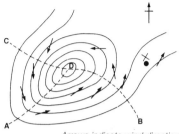

Arrows indicate wind direction

Troughs of low pressure

In most depressions the cloud and rain tend to be concentrated in bands extending outwards from somewhere near the centre. These bands of weather may be from 10 to 200 miles wide and are called **troughs of low pressure** because the pressure is lower along them than at other points the same distance from the centre of the depression. There is a very definite relation between pressure and wind; the wind blows according to the gradient of pressure. The greater the fall of pressure from one point to the next the stronger the wind between the two points. So with a trough of low pressure; the more marked it is, the stronger the winds associated with it and the greater the change in the wind direction from one side of it to the other.

The simple diagram above will help to make this point clearer.

D marks the centre of a depression. The line DA marks the axis of a **vigorous** trough of low pressure in which there is a change of wind of over 90 degrees as you go from one side to the other, you would expect a lot of rain mainly on the forward side of it. DB marks a less vigorous trough, but still with a quite a marked wind change and probably a fair amount of cloud and rain. DC is a relatively **weak** trough with comparatively little wind change and probably only occasional rain or a belt of showers.

Depressions can move in any direction but most frequently from west to east. Whether the depression is moving or not, its troughs will usually be circulating round its centre. If you are at X and the trough moves across you, you can see from the diagram that the winds will back and increase as the trough approaches and veer as it passes. The passage of even the weakest trough may make a lot of difference to your attempt to round a windward mark. If you are at X and the depression moves ENE to the north of you, the wind will veer from southerly ahead of the low to northerly behind it. The veer is unlikely to be steady and will in fact be concentrated in the passage of the troughs, while ahead of the troughs you may experience a temporary backing of the wind. This is typical of what is met with in practice, but there are an awful lot of variations on the theme. Finally, if you are at X and the depression moves ESE keeping its centre south of you, the winds will back from southerly to northerly. Any troughs will again be an added complication.

Troughs may fill or deepen independently of the parent depression, and sometimes a deepening trough will develop its own circulation and a new low is formed – a **secondary depression**.

Fronts

There is little that need be said about fronts because they are simply a particular type of trough of low pressure, and troughs have been discussed in the previous paragraph. A **front** is, in fact, a trough of low pressure in which there is a change in air mass from one side to the other. In a **warm front** the air mass changes from cold to warm as the warm frontal trough passes, and in a **cold front** the air mass changes from warm to cold as it passes. The troughs at DB and DA are typical positions for warm and cold fronts respectively in the circulation of a depression, with the warm air in between them. Troughs in which there is an air mass change are usually more vigorous than those in which there is none. In fact wherever you find an air mass change you will usually find some sort of trough of low pressure. Fronts have a number of typical weather characteristics which are discussed in most books on the weather. Their wind change characteristics are the same as for the trough. Incidentally, in land area forecasts, fronts are rarely mentioned and are usually referred to as troughs. The same sometimes applies in the shipping forecasts.

Anticyclone

The word anticyclone obviously means something contrasting with cyclone. An anticyclone or high has a **high** central pressure relative to its surroundings, fair or fine weather and light winds circulating clockwise around the centre in the northern hemisphere and anti-clockwise in the southern, and blowing slightly outwards. They vary in size from perhaps 200 miles across for the small high that accidentally finds itself between two lows, to some 2,500 miles across for some of the large and very persistent anticyclones which are responsible for the longer spells of dry weather. An anticyclone is said to **build** if its pressure is rising and to **decline** or **weaken** if its pressure is falling. If the pressure is falling very quickly it is said to be **collapsing**. Large anticyclones are usually slow-moving but some of the smaller ones which occur between depressions move quickly – perhaps as fast as 30 to 40 knots. More often, between depressions, instead of a high, with a closed circulation, one finds a **ridge of high pressure**. This is analogous to a mountain ridge between two hollows. Similarly a weak ridge may well occur between two troughs (or valleys) even in the circulation of a depression. The weather in a ridge is similar to the weather in an anticyclone though it may not last as long. In a weak ridge between two fast moving troughs it may be little more than a bright period.

As you move outwards from the centre of an anticyclone or away from the axis of a ridge the winds usually increase. If a ridge is crossing your course the winds will decrease as it approaches, back as it passes and then increase and continue to back depending on what is coming next.

The following terms are used in bulletins to describe the speed of movement of pressure systems:

Slowly	up to 15 knots
Steadily	15 – 25 knots
Rather quickly	25 – 35 knots
Rapidly	35 – 45 knots
Very rapidly	over 45 knots

STANDARD DEFINITIONS OF STATE OF SEA

Sea state	Height of waves in metres	Definition English	French
0	0	calm – glassy	calme – plate
1	0 to 0.1	calm – rippled	calme – ridée
2	0.1 to 0.5	smooth	belle
3	0.5 to 1.25	slight	peu agitée
4	1.25 to 2.5	moderate	agitée
5	2.5 to 4	rough	forte
6	4 to 6	very rough	très forte
7	6 to 9	high	grosse
8	9 to 14	very high	très grosse
9	over 14	phenomenal	énorme

WRITING DOWN THE SHIPPING BULLETIN

Shipping bulletins are broadcast at normal reading speed so it is necessary to have a prepared form with at least all the sea areas listed and some form of shorthand notation for the majority of the standard words and phrases. Forms suitable for recording shipping forecasts are available from the RYA and the Royal Meteorological Society, Reading RG1 7LL. There is nothing to stop you devising your own shorthand so long as you can remember afterwards the meaning of what you have written, but there is a lot to be said for using a notation which has been evolved by those with considerable experience in using shipping bulletins and which includes a number of the standard international weather map symbols. Once you are familiar with the more common of these international symbols you will be able to appreciate at a glance the information on any weather map which you may see displayed in clubs or at ports of call.

The general synopsis

Few international symbols are involved here except of course for the points of the compass – N, S, NW, SW, etc – but it is not possible to write down the synopsis until you have practised a simple shorthand using initial letters for terms such as depression, anticyclone, low, high, warm front, cold front, occlusion, trough, ridge etc., and for the various sea areas which are usually referred to in giving the positions of the weather systems. One very useful hint is to use an oblique stroke to denote the passage of time, and this applies particularly to the sea area forecasts as we shall see. Also it is often a good idea to denote movement by an arrow.

The sea area forecast

Wind – The simplest forecast is in the form 'northwest 5', which is obviously abbreviated as 'NW 5'. Often however we have something like 'northwest 4 to 5 at first, backing southwest and increasing to 7 to gale 8 by end of the period' which should be written as 'NW 4–5/SW 7–8', and all the rest of the words can be inferred from this simple shorthand form. Note particularly the use of an oblique stroke to distinguish between 'at first' and 'later'. 'In the South at first' abbreviates to 'In S/' whereas 'In the South later' would abbreviate to '/in S'. The words 'temporarily', 'occasionally', 'locally' are often used and should be abbreviated to 'tem', 'occ', 'loc'.

Weather – This is always given in terms such as 'fair', 'showers', 'rain' etc. Here international shorthand should be used and you can choose between the Beaufort letter notation or the international weather map symbols as given opposite. There is something to be said for using the international map symbols because you can then plot these directly onto your map, but the former are much easier to learn and you can readily turn them into plotting symbols at your leisure after the broadcast. The phrases 'at first' and 'later' are often used and, again, an oblique stroke comes in very useful. For instance 'rain at first, showers later' can be abbreviated to 'r/p'. This sort of detail should always be taken down as it almost certainly ties in with a change of wind and the passage of an important weather system through the sea area.

Abridged Beaufort weather notation and international plotting symbols

Beaufort letter		Plotting symbol
r	rain	●
d	drizzle	❥
s	snow	✳
p	shower	▽
h	hail	△
th	thunderstorm	⟨
q	squall	Ⅴ
m	mist	=
f	fog	≡
z	haze	∞

For heavy precipitation, capital letters are used e.g. R – heavy rain.

Visibility – A straightforward abbreviation of 'g' for 'good', 'm' for 'moderate', 'p' for 'poor' is all that is required here, remembering again to use a vertical stroke to denote a passage of time and also to take down all the details which are given about fog. Fog will be discussed in more detail later under the discussion on weather hazards beginning on page 23.

Coastal station reports

As with the sea area forecasts you need a prepared form with the coastal stations already listed, and columns for the reports which are always given for each station in the sequence wind, significant weather (fair and fine are not 'significant' and are not mentioned – if nothing is said about the weather you should assume that it is fair or fine), visibility in miles or metres, barometric pressure in millibars, and finally pressure tendency (i.e. whether the barometer is rising or falling, and how rapidly, or whether it is steady). The same shorthand should be used as for the sea area forecasts.

There is no need to write down the words miles or metres as one or two figures will always be miles and three or four figures will always be metres. The pressure tendency should be abbreviated to s for steady, r for rising, rs for rising slowly, etc: or you can use a stroke inclined at various angles according to the way you would observe the pressure tendency on a barograph. The definitions of the terms used for pressure tendency are given on page 15.

USING THE SHIPPING FORECAST AND OTHER WEATHER BULLETINS

Write down at least the General Synopsis, the forecast for the sea areas in which you will be sailing, the forecast for adjacent sea areas, the reports from coastal stations nearest to your area, and the outlook from the land area forecast. If you are sailing close inshore write down also the regional land area forecast particularly details about the wind.

Having got all this information you can use it to decide the best strategy and tactics. Whether you are ocean racing or merely crossing Lyme Bay, if you set off on the wrong tack for an expected change in wind it can cost you many hours.

If you are under power and fail to appreciate that a wind change is going to coincide with an adverse tide it can give you a most uncomfortable and perhaps dangerous short steep sea, or make it impossible to cross the bar when you were intending to make port before dark.

Many such situations can be avoided by careful attention to the weather forecasts. The weather can change very quickly. Forecasts are on the air at least every six hours and you should listen to all of them. If your radio goes wrong put into harbour for repairs.

The following example will show you the sort of detail which you can glean from careful attention to the shipping bulletin.

The morning Shipping Forecast included the following:

General Synopsis – 'a trough of low pressure will move eastwards across the British Isles and is expected to lie from Viking to German Bight at midnight tonight'.

Sea Area Forecast – 'Humber, Thames, Dover – southwest veering northwest, 4 or 5; rain or drizzle followed by showers; moderate or poor with fog patches, becoming good'.

'Wight, Portland – southwest veering northwest, 3 to 4; rain or drizzle then showers; visibility moderate or poor with fog patches, becoming good'.

'Plymouth – northwest, 3 or 4; showers becoming fair; good'.

Let us assume that you are hoping to sail in sea area Dover. The wind force given for the group of areas which includes Dover is 4 or 5 but since the next group to Dover is given as 3 or 4 we can infer that the wind in Dover is likely to be at the Force 4 end of the range.

The southwesterly wind is obviously associated with the rain, drizzle and fog patches ahead of the trough of low pressure, and the northwesterly wind with the showers and good visibility behind the trough. The trough has all the characteristics of a cold front. The forecast of northwesterly winds for Plymouth tells us that the trough is already past that area and we can infer that it is moving over the western edge of Portland. We are told that it will be over German Bight by midnight so we can interpolate its movement between these two sea areas and get a reasonably good forecast of its time of crossing sea area Dover. Hence we can derive our own forecast of the time of veer of wind in Dover and the time of clearance of the rain, drizzle and fog. We can in fact plan a fair passage across the Channel from late morning onwards with a following wind, good visibility and just a few showers. The coastal stations reports from south coast stations would be found to confirm the inference as to the present position of the trough.

The more you practise using the shipping forecasts the more interesting and useful you will find the bulletins and reports from all sources, even those for the more remote areas such as southeast Iceland. Each item of information becomes a piece in a jig-saw which you need to complete the whole picture.

But what if your sources of information disagree or are inconsistent? Suppose Jersey Radio gives a different forecast from Niton, or Schevenigen tells a different story from North

Foreland. It is no use denying that this happens. It does. But do not despair. Remember two things. First, that both forecasts must be based on the same initial data – they cannot be contrary in that sense; second that you already have, or should have, a good idea as to what the weather chart looks like in terms of depressions and anticyclones, troughs and ridges. This cannot be in dispute. So you, with your weather map in front of you, are in a good position to sort out for yourself what is the best possible forecast for your own particular area. You can even try to identify the reasons for the two divergent forecasts in terms of what is happening on the chart. And what is even more important, the lapse of time since the forecast was prepared means that you have additional information in terms of the weather you have observed and are observing which will help you to sort out the answer. What is the barometer doing, the wind, the cloud, and the sea. Even the smallest amount of information is all part of the overall pattern of movement and change in the atmosphere. And if you can go even a small way to understanding it, it will provide a new dimension to life afloat.

Reading wind speed and direction from weather maps

Many weather maps have a scale of wind speed in one corner called the 'geostrophic scale' (see illustration). Using a pair of dividers, take the distance between adjacent isobars on the weather map over the area of interest and read from the scale the wind speed for the latitude of the area. This is the actual or predicted wind speed at a height of about 500 metres. The wind on the water is some 10% to 20% less than this. If you are sailing in different latitudes it is important to appreciate that for a given isobar spacing (pressure

GEOSTROPHIC WIND SCALE
IN KNOTS FOR 4 MB INTERVALS

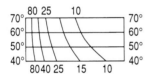

SCALE OF NAUTICAL MILES

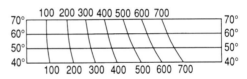

gradient) the wind is much stronger in low latitudes compared to high latitudes.

The reading of the wind from the geostrophic scale for a given latitude and pressure gradient is always the same for the same map projection and scale. So it is worth cutting one out, and using for instance the wind speed scale from a map on the MetFAX Aviation menu to read the wind from any other maps having the same scale, which includes many of those on MetFAX Marine. Alternatively use the scales above. Measure the distance apart of isobars at 4mb intervals in miles on any weather map; set your dividers to this distance on the scale on the right. Transfer this setting to the scale on the left for the appropriate latitude and read off the wind speed.

No scale is needed to read the wind direction from a weather map. The wind on the water is the direction given by the run of the isobars less about 15 degrees.

Metmap forms for constructing your own weather map are available in pads of 40, price £5.25 plus 50p postage from:- RYA, Romsey Road, Eastleigh, Hants SO50 9YA.

More detailed guidance will be found in *Weather at Sea* (see page 4).

COASTAL WINDS

Winds within about 10 miles of the coast are influenced by the contours of the nearby land, by the local generation of the sea and land breezes, by the state of the tide, and by the fact that air blowing over water is subject to a different frictional force from air blowing over land. These coastal influences may cause a difference of as much as 10 to 15 knots in the wind at points only a few kilometres apart, even when the coast is fairly flat. Near mountains a local increase of 20-30 knots is not uncommon.

Sea and land breezes

Sea breezes develop when the land becomes warmer than the sea, and the direction of the pressure gradient wind is from land to sea. Typically on a bright or sunny day an offshore wind at breakfast time drops to calm near the coast, and is followed by an onshore sea breeze which increases steadily, veers, extends seawards, and may reach Force 6 close to the coast by mid-afternoon.

When the gradient wind is onshore and the day is bright or sunny the wind will either increase or decrease a few knots by afternoon depending on whether the land is to the left or right of the wind direction looking downwind.

Land breezes are experienced at night. They are strongest under clear skies and at the mouths of valleys.

Frictional effects

Land, particularly where there are trees and buildings, exerts a drag on the air. The drag over the water is much less. These frictional forces not only slow the air down but also cause a change of direction, and the direction over the water is about 15° different from the direction over the land. Winds blowing nearly parallel to the coast will converge or diverge depending on whether the greater friction is to the right or left of the wind direction. With convergence (east winds on a south facing coast, west winds on a north facing coast, etc) a band of stronger winds is experienced within about three miles of the coast; up to 10 knots stronger in some cases. Conversely with divergence (west winds on a south facing coast, etc) winds may be that much lighter near the coast, except when land or sea breezes are blowing.

Tidal effects

A change in tide may influence the wind due to:

- a change in friction as the height and length of the wave changes
- a change in water temperature, particularly near an estuary
- a change in temperature of sandbanks or mud flats as they emerge from or disappear beneath the water

More detailed information will be found in *Wind Strategy* Second Edition 1992 by David Houghton in the *Sail to Win* Series published by Fernhurst Books.

WEATHER HAZARDS

GALES

Gales which are due to depressions do not spring up without any warning. All inshore sailors can avoid them and so too can many offshore sailors. Squalls and thunderstorms are a different matter and will be discussed later.

How does one receive warning of an approaching gale? The most obvious answer is to keep a listening watch on Radio 4 or the nearest coast radio station. The battery power consumption of most modern radios is very small but carry spare batteries just in case. If you need to save power then switch in to Radio 4 on the hour or to the coast radio at the end of each silence period (3 and 33 minutes past each hour) – you will need an alarm clock to remind you.

Your barometer or barograph will also give you good warning of an approaching gale. A fall of pressure of over 8 millibars in 3 hours is almost certain to be followed by a gale whatever your wind is to start with, and a fall of pressure of over 5 millibars in 3 hours is almost certain to be followed by a Force 6 (the yachtsman's gale). If your wind is Force 3 or less when you observe these tendencies your barometer will have given you about 4 to 8 hours warning. A very rapid rise in pressure after a trough has passed is also indicative of a gale and the same figures apply – a rise of over 8 millibars in 3 hours for a Force 8 and over 5 millibars in 3 hours for a Force 6. You must of course make allowances for your own movement, either towards or away from the depression. Buy's Ballots Law – if you stand with your back to the wind low pressure is on your left hand side – will tell you which way you are going relative to the depression.

If the barometer is falling rapidly and clouds are increasing rapidly – particularly if the upper clouds are moving fast and are well veered to the surface winds – then fear the worst and do not be caught on a lee shore. Slower changes in the barometer reading do not necessarily preclude a gale, but they are less definitive.

STRONG LOCAL WINDS

If the wind is blowing almost parallel to the coast, or at an angle of up to about 25 degrees, then be prepared for a local increase of wind up to 10 miles from the coast. This is especially marked on the edges of anticyclones when a local increase of over 10 knots may occur. For instance, an easterly wind blowing down the English Channel in the circulation of an anticyclone to the north, while only Force 4 over most of the Channel, may be Force 6 or even 7 along the English coast. An outstanding example is with a northeasterly over Biscay when an increase of as much as 20 knots frequently occurs off Cape Finisterre.

Another wind which needs watching is the sea breeze. On a sunny summer's day, if conditions are right, the sea breeze may enhance the actual wind to give a local increase of a good 10 knots just along the coast. A gentle breeze in a warm and sheltered harbour is often unrepresentative of conditions out at sea.

SQUALLS AND THUNDERSTORMS

The arched line of black cloud associated with a squall can usually be seen as it approaches and so it gives its own warning, but only a brief one, of about half an hour. The only thing to do is to reef and make for the lightest part of the cloud. Having weathered the squall you can usually take it that another one is unlikely for 4 to 6 hours.

The advancing dark mass of threatening cloud associated with a mature thunderstorm is distinguishable from that of an advancing depression by the lack of freshening wind and sea ahead of it. In fact, it is often heralded by a decrease in wind and an almost glassy sea. The best rule is to sail so as to leave the storm to port. By doing so, although you may not miss the associated squalls you should miss the worst of them. Your barometer or barograph will show very erratic pressure changes in a thunderstorm, jumping down and up by a millibar or two.

FOG

Two types of fog must be distinguished, land and sea fog.

Land or radiation fog

This is fog which forms over the land on a clear night. It may drift seawards from the coast but does not usually go far before dispersing, and rarely more than 2 to 3 miles from the shore. What is more, as soon as it hits the sea, it starts clearing near the surface and by the time it is 100 metres offshore it is usually clear to about mast height. So if the forecast is for fog over land, clearing during the morning, you can safely go out to sea expecting the fog to be gone by the time you return to port.

Sea fog

This is one of the worst hazards at sea and forms when warm moist air is carried by the wind over a relatively cold sea. The criterion for sea fog to form is when the dewpoint of the air is equal to or above the sea surface temperature. In winter and spring the sea is coldest inshore so fog forms more frequently along the coast than out to sea. In summer and autumn the sea is coldest away from the shore so fog forms more frequently out at sea. There are always variations in sea temperature from place to place and consequently variations in the extent of sea fog.

If the dewpoint of the air being blown across the sea is very high, and everywhere the sea temperature is lower, then **widespread fog** or **extensive fog** is forecast. If the dewpoint of the air is only a little above sea temperature and in some places may not be so, then **fog banks** are forecast. If the dewpoint of the air is only above the sea temperature in some places then **fog patches** are forecast, or, in winter and spring just coastal fog if that is appropriate.

HURRICANES

Hurricane is the name given to a tropical cyclone when it occurs in the North Atlantic or north-east Pacific. It is synonymous with a cyclone in the Indian Ocean and a typhoon in other parts of the Pacific.

STEEP WAVES

Dangerously steep waves are encountered when the wind is blowing against the current. Around Britain the danger lasts typically for 2 or 3 hours around the maximum tidal stream, given a contrary wind. A much publicised example was the 1998 Sydney-Hobart race when a new vigourous depression with 50 knots southerly winds moved over the 3 knot south going East Australian current. Considerable damage and loss of life ensued.

SOURCES, CONTENT, MAPS & TABLES

INTERNET – SELECTION OF WEATHER SITES FOR THE MARINER

Met Office

The Met Office has several pages of useful information for the mariner, much of which is free of charge. There are added value products available via the Met WEB pages, these pages containing similar information to that available via the Met Office MetFAX service. Full details can be found by following the link to MetWEB.

Met Office home page
http://www.metoffice.com

Index for Leisure marine products
http://www.metoffice.com/leisuremarine/index.html

Index for weather maps and satellite pictures
http://www.metoffice.com/weather/index.html

The Shipping Forecast from the Met Office
http://www.metoffice.com/datafiles/offshore.html

The Inshore Waters Forecast (16-area forecast) from the Met Office
http://www.metoffice.com/datafiles/inshore.html

Latest Gale Warning issued by the Met Office
http://www.metoffice.com/cgi-bin/GaleWarn

Listing of links to marine products

The site maintained by Martin Stubbs provides access to marine forecasts world-wide and other related information such as links to weather charts of interest to the mariner. There is also a section on how to obtain marine forecasts by e-mail – a not-too-expensive way of obtaining forecasts on the high seas.
http://www.users.zetnet.co.uk/tempusfugit/marine

Frank Singleton's site for small craft owners – contains a wealth of information on accessing weather related sites of interest to the mariner. In particular, there are pages explaining how to access GRIB data at sea for display on a lap-top computer (GRIB data files of forecasts, for example wind forecasts, can be accessed using e-mail at sea and displayed using a suitable viewer).
http://www.franksingleton.clara.net

Selection of other links to marine related weather information

Irish coastal waters: Shipping forecast and latest gale warning via Met Eireann
http://www.met.ie/forecasts/seaarea.asp

Météo-France – marine home page (now in English)
http://www.meteo.fr/meteonet_en/temps/activite/mer/cotes/cot.htm

Jersey Met – a good site for weather in and around the Channel Islands
http://www.jerseymet.gov.je

Reports from buoys (hourly), light vessels and ship reports
http://www.ndbc.noaa.gov/Maps/United_Kingdom.shtml

Latest actual and forecast charts via Köln University
http://www.uni-koeln.de/math-nat-fak/geomet/meteo/winfos/index-e.html

European Centre (ECMWF) – medium-range forecast charts (days 3 to 76) available
http://www.ecmwf.int

Satellite Imagery

Dundee University provides access to world-wide real-time imagery (NOAA and Geostationery) (*note one must register, but registration is free*)
http://www.sat.dundee.ac.uk/

European Space Agency for Meteosat imagery
http://www.eumetsat.de/en/

STATIONS WHOSE LATEST WEATHER REPORTS ARE BROADCAST IN BBC RADIO 4 SHIPPING BULLETINS

Lerwick

* *Automatic stations whose reports do not include weather, ie if there is rain, drizzle, showers and so on.*

Stornoway

Tiree *

Malin Head LH

Fife Ness

Ronaldsway

Bridlington

Valentia

Sandettie Light Vessel *

Scilly *

Greenwich Light Vessel *

Channel Light Vessel *

Jersey

STATIONS WHOSE LATEST WEATHER REPORTS ARE BROADCAST IN BBC RADIO 4 INSHORE WATERS BULLETINS

Lerwick

Stornoway

Wick *

Aberdeen

Leuchars

Machrihanish

Greenock

Boulmer

Larne

Ronaldsway

Bridlington

Valley

Liverpool (Crosby)

Aberporth

Milford Haven

Sheerness

Scilly *

St Catherines Point *

Jersey

* Automatic stations whose reports do not include weather, ie if there is rain, drizzle, showers and so on.

FORECASTS AND WARNINGS VIA COASTGUARD

MCA Search and Rescue Centres provide a comprehensive broadcast service of warnings of gales, strong wind warnings, sea area forecasts and forecasts for inshore waters. Warnings are broadcast on receipt and repeated (while still in operation) in the following four-hourly scheduled broadcasts of warnings, forecasts and navigational warnings. See page 38 for more details.

Telephone numbers & initial weather broadcasting times are shown on the map below.

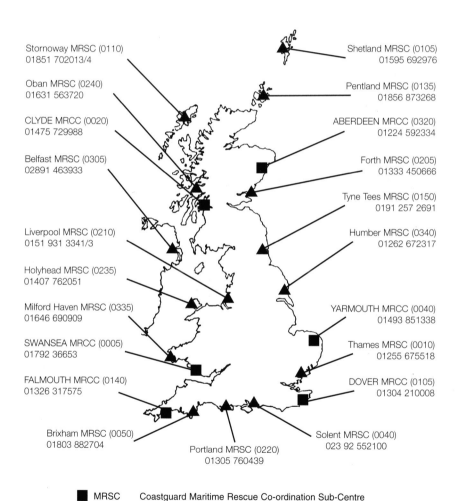

Stornoway MRSC (0110)
01851 702013/4

Oban MRSC (0240)
01631 563720

CLYDE MRCC (0020)
01475 729988

Belfast MRSC (0305)
02891 463933

Liverpool MRSC (0210)
0151 931 3341/3

Holyhead MRSC (0235)
01407 762051

Milford Haven MRSC (0335)
01646 690909

SWANSEA MRCC (0005)
01792 36653

FALMOUTH MRCC (0140)
01326 317575

Brixham MRSC (0050)
01803 882704

Shetland MRSC (0105)
01595 692976

Pentland MRSC (0135)
01856 873268

ABERDEEN MRCC (0320)
01224 592334

Forth MRSC (0205)
01333 450666

Tyne Tees MRSC (0150)
0191 257 2691

Humber MRSC (0340)
01262 672317

YARMOUTH MRCC (0040)
01493 851338

Thames MRSC (0010)
01255 675518

DOVER MRCC (0105)
01304 210008

Solent MRSC (0040)
023 92 552100

Portland MRSC (0220)
01305 760439

■ MRSC   Coastguard Maritime Rescue Co-ordination Sub-Centre
▲ MRCC   Coastguard Maritime Rescue Co-ordination Centre

FORECASTS & WEATHER REPORTS BY TELEPHONE & FAX

Marinecall and MetFAX Marine (see page 7)

Service/product	Phone/fax number	Update times			
Marinecall					
Telephone 2-day forecast	09068 500 XXX	0700	1900		
	or 09068 110 010 and follow voice menu				
Telephone 3 to 5-day forecast	09068 500 XXX				
UK National inshore	450	0800			
English Channel	992				
Southern North Sea	991				
Irish Sea	954				
Northern North Sea	955				
Northwest Scotland	985				
Biscay	953				
Telephone latest weather reports	09068 110 010	hourly			
MetFAX Marine					
Fax Index Page	09060 100 401				
Fax 2-day inshore forecast plus latest weather maps	09060 100 XXX	0700	1900		
Fax 3 to 5-day planner plus latest weather maps					
UK National	09060 100 450	0500			
Biscay	470	0800			
English Channel	471	0800			
Southern North Sea	472	0800			
Irish Sea	473	0800			
N W Scottish waters	468	0800			
Northern North Sea	469	0800			
Fax 24-hour shipping forecast	09060 100 441	0030	0600	1400	1800
Latest actual weather map*	444	0340	0940	1540	2140
24-hour forecast weather map*	445	0600	1100	1645	2245
Chart of latest UK weather reports*	447	0030	then every 3hrs		
Latest satellite picture*	499	0730	1330	1930	
2, 3, 4 & 5-day forecast charts	426	0700	1900		
Chart of latest European weather reports	474	0100	0700	1300	1900

Other MetFax services

For index pages dial:

All MetFAX services	09060 100 400
MetFAX Aviation	09060 700 501
MetFAX Education	09003 400 480

XXX   Dial the 3 figures appropriate to the area you want – see Marinecall area map and list overleaf.

*   Update times one hour later when British Summer Time in force.

Met Office Customer Centre

Telephone	0845 300 0300
Fax	0845 300 1300
Email	sales@metoffice.com

Marinecall and MetFAX Marine coastal areas numbers

451	Scotland North
452	Scotland East
453	North East
454	East
455	Anglia
456	Channel East
457	Mid-Channel
458	South West
459	Bristol Channel
460	Wales
461	North West
462	Clyde
463	Caledonia
464	Minch
465	Ulster
432	Channel Isles (Marinecall)
466	Channel Isles (MetFAX)

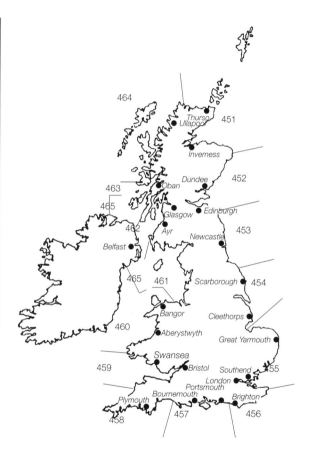

Summary

Telephone forecasts	09068 500 + area number
Forecasts or reports	09068 110 010 and follow menu
Fax forecasts	09060 100 + area number

Calls on 09068 are charged at 60p per minute at all times.

Calls on 09060 are charged at £1 per minute. Transmission is at 9600 baud.

3 to 5-day Planning Forecast Areas
Dial code plus area number

Marinecall 09068 500 XXX

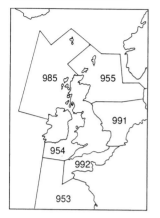

MetFAX Marine 09060 100 XXX

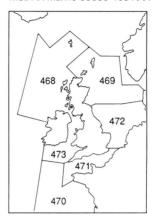

MARINE MOBILE SERVICES

1. Register online at www.metoffice.com or via the Met Office Customer Centre on: 0845 300 0300.

2. Once you have registered you will be sent a text message welcoming you to the Met Office mobile services. When you receive this message send the message 'MET OK' to 07712 396853 to activate your account.

3. Credit your account with a credit card either online using the secure site or by calling the Met Office Customer Centre.

Requesting a Time and Place Forecast

1. Set up your personal preferences via www.metoffice.com by entering the latitude and longitude of relevant points on your route and naming them.

2. Set up the services to be sent automatically to your phone ('push' messages), or request a message as and when you need one ('pull' messages).

3. Type in a text message, which always starts MET<space> TPF <space> Enter the time <space> Enter the name of the location you have set up via the website.

4. Send to: 07712 396853.

Price: 20p SMS and WAP, for 'push' messages, or 50p on SMS and WAP for 'pull' messages.

Requesting the latest Shipping Forecast
Text message: MET SAF + command code

Send to: 07712 396853

Price: 10p SMS and FREE on WAP

Requesting a Gale Warning
Text message: MET SAG + command code

Send to: 07712 396853

Price: 10p SMS and FREE on WAP

Sea area	Command code	Sea area	Command code
Viking	4411	Plymouth	4426
North Utsire	4412	Biscay	4427
South Utsire	4413	FitzRoy	4428
Forties	4414	Sole	4429
Cromarty	4415	Lundy	4430
Forth	4416	Fastnet	4431
Tyne	4417	Irish Sea	4432
Dogger	4418	Shannon	4433
Fisher	4419	Rockall	4434
German Bight	4420	Malin	4435
Humber	4421	Bebrides	4436
Thames	4422	Bailey	4437
Dover	4423	Fair Isle	4438
Wight	4424	Faeroes	4439
Portland	4425	South East Iceland	4440

Requesting an Inshore Waters Forecast

Test message: MET IWF + command code

Send to 07712 396853

Price: 50p on SMS and WAP

Location	Command Code
General situation	MET IWF1000
Cape Wrath to Dunscansby Head, including Orkney	MET IWF1001
Shetland	MET IWF1002
Dunscansby Head to Whitby	MET IWF1003
Whitby to North Foreland	MET IWF1004
North Foreland to St. Catherine's Point	MET IWF1005
St. Catherine's Point to Lands End	MET IWF1006
Lands End to Colwyn Bay	MET IWF1007
Colwyn Bay to Mull of Kintyre inlcuding Lough Foyle to Carlingford Lough	MET IWF1008
Mull of Kintyre to Cape Wrath	MET IWF1009

Requesting the latest coastal station report

Text message: MET CRA + command code

Send to: 07712 396853

Price: 30p SMS and WAP

Location	Command Code
Ballycastle, Bangor Harbour	MET CRA4301
Oban, Greenock	MET CRA4302
South Uist, Tiree	MET CRA4303
Aultbea, Stornoway	MET CRA4304
Machrihanish, Prestwick	MET CRA4305
Walney Island, St Bees Head	MET CRA4306
Rhyl, Crosby	MET CRA4307
Aberdaron, Valley	MET CRA4308
Aberporth, Milford Haven	MET CRA4309
Cardiff, Mumbles	MET CRA4310
Falmouth, Scilly-St Mary's	MET CRA4311
Brixham, Plymouth	MET CRA4312
Channel L/V, Guernsey	MET CRA4313
Jersey, Bréhat	MET CRA4314
Thorney Island, Lee-on-Solent	MET CRA4315
St Catherine's Point, Greenwich L/V	MET CRA4316
Dover	MET CRA4317
Walton-on-the-Naze, Sheerness	MET CRA4318
Weybourne, Holbeach	MET CRA4319
Bridlington, Donna Nook	MET CRA4320
Aberdeen, Fife Ness	MET CRA4322
Peterhead, Lossiemouth	MET CRA4323
Sule Skerry, Wick	MET CRA4324

'Talk to a Forecaster'

This interactive fax or phone service includes the opportunity to speak with a forecaster and is accessible from anywhere in the world. Payment is online by credit card. Fax charts cost £3 and consultation with a forecaster a flat rate of £17.

Full information and a menu can be obtained free by dialling 08700 767 888.

There is a helpline on 0845 300 0 300.

Mediterranean Forecast Service

To consult a marine forecaster about the weather in the Mediterranean phone:

44 (0)870 0 767 888 Calls are charged at a flat rate of £15.00.

Forecasts for Spain and the Balearics are available by fax on the same number at a charge of £3 each chart.

To obtain Mediterranean forecasts from the UK dial 09060 100 plus area code below. They are currently limited to the Balearics and the eastern coastal waters of Spain.

435	Gibraltar to Malaga		438	Valencia to Barcelona
436	Malaga to Cartagena		439	Balearic Islands
437	Cartagena to Valencia			

Weathercall

Dialling prefix 09068 505

401	London		416	N W England
402	Kent, Sussex, Surrey		417	W & S Yorks & Peak District
403	Dorset & Hants		418	N E England
404	Devon & Cornwall		419	Cumbria, incl Lake District
405	Wilts, Gloucs, Avon & Somerset		420	S W Scotland
406	Berks, Bucks & Oxon		421	W Central Scotland
407	Beds, Herts & Essex		422	Ed'burgh, S Fife, Lothian & Borders
408	Norfolk, Suffolk & Cambs		423	E Central Scotland
409	West Mid, Sth Glam & Gwent		424	Grampian & E Highlands
410	Shrops, Hereford & Worcester		425	N W Scotland
411	Central Midlands		426	Caithness, Orkney & Shetland
412	East Midlands		427	N Ireland
413	Lincs & Humberside		430	National 3 to 5 day outlook
414	Dyfed & Powys			
415	Gwynedd & Clwyd			

Weather routeing

Specialist marine weather routeing services are available from:-

MetWorks Limited

MetWorks Ltd provides a full weather routeing service which includes an initial advisory service, regular recommendations and advice on optimum routes, and frequent forecasts along the vessel's track, extending to five days ahead. Forecasting and routeing services can be supplied to luxury charter and private yachts of any type. MetWorks services are based on advanced software working with data supplied under contract by the UK Met office.

For further information contact:

Acorn House, 43 Longshot Lane, Bracknell, Berkshire

United Kingdom RG12 1RL

Tel: +44(0)1344 411116 Fax: +44(0)1344 317654

Email: ops@metworksltd.com (FAO Captain Gordon V Mackie, Managing Director)

Noble Denton Weather Services Limited

Noble Denton's Forecast Centre in central London operates 24-hours a day, every day of the year and routinely receives global meteorological data including the output from several computer models of the atmosphere. Their Weather Consultancy Service also provides up-to-date weather forecasts for any location in the UK or Europe, either onshore or offshore.

For further information contact:

Noble Denton Weather Services Limited,
Noble House, 131 Aldersgate Street, London EC1A 4EB
Tel: 0207 606 4961 Fax: 0207 606 0773
Email: fcst@ndws.demon.co.uk

WNI Ocean Routes (UK) Ltd

The world's largest privately owned weather forecasting company employs nearly 700 people in 11 countries, and still provides localised services.

For further information contact:

WNI Ocean routes (UK), Weather News House,
Harenes Circle, Altens, Aberdeen AB12 3LY
Tel: +44 1224 248080 Fax: 441224 248250
Email: sales.abd@wni.com Web: www.oceanroutes.co.uk

TELEPHONE WEATHER SERVICES ABROAD

France

France Telecom and Meteo-France operate an automatic telephone weather service - ALLO METEO FRANCE - with a universal number, the forecast heard depending on the area in which you call as follows:

Service	Telephone number
National forecast	08 92 68 01 01
Regional forecast	08 92 68 00 00
Departmental forecast	08 92 68 02 XX (XX is the local departmental code)
Mountain forecast	08 92 68 04 04
Marine forecast	08 92 68 08 08
Marine local coastal forecast	08 92 68 08 XX (see below)

While the marine forecast service number 08 36 68 08 08 is universally valid and provides a fairly detailed local coastal forecast, a more detailed menu is available.

The following is a selection; prefixed in each case by 08 36 68 08.

Coastal Zone	Telephone number	Coastal Zone	Telephone number
Pas de Calais	08 92 68 08 59 or 62	Gironde	33
Somme estuary	80	Landes	40
Seine estuary	76	Pyrénées Atlantiques	64
Calvados	14	**Mediterranean**	
Cotentin	50	Cerbère à Narbonne to	08 92 68 08 66 or 11
Ille et Vilaine	35	The Balearics	
Côtes d'Armor	22	Narbonne to Port Camargue	30 or 34 or 11
Finistère	29	Mouth of the Rhône	30 or 13
Morbihan	56	Var	83
Loire-Atlantique	44	Alpes Maritimes	06
Vendée	85	Corsica, east and west coasts	20
Charente maritime	17		

The cost of this service is independent of distance and at a universal rate of 0.34 euro per minute.

Germany

The Deutscher Wetterdienst provides a telephone weather warnings service which can be accessed from outside the country if required. The number is (49) 40 319 66 28. If there is no warning in operation a wind forecast is given for German Bight and the west and south Baltic

Ireland

The latest sea area forecast and gale warnings for Irish coasts are available on the Weatherdial Service by calling 1550 123 855

Spain

The Spanish Instituo Nacional de Meteorologica provides a recorded telephone marine weather information service. Numbers (sea area map on page 57) are:

906 365 371	High seas bulletin for Alboran, Palos, Argelia, Baleares and Golfo de Leon.
	Coastal waters bulletin for Mediterranean coasts.
906 365 372	High seas bulletin for Gran Sol, Vizcaya, Cantabrico, Finisterre.
	Coastal waters bulletin for the coasts of Guipuzcoa, Vizcaya, Cantabria, Asturias, Lugo, Coruña, Pontevedra.
906 365 373	High seas bulletin for San Vincente, Azores, Canarias, Sahara, Golfo de Cadiz and Alboran.
	Coastal waters bulletin for coasts of Huelva, Cadiz, Ceuta, Malaga, Melilla, Granada, Almeria and Canary Islands.
906 365 370	Balearic Islands.

RADIO FACSIMILE AND TELEX BROADCASTS

Bracknell GFA has closed, but there are still several broadcasts which include information accessible while at sea. The following is a brief summary (time in GMT, frequencies in kHz) - see also page 25 for details of a website providing access to the latest schedules.

Northwood (GB) - (Fax)

Frequencies	2618.5	4610	8040	11086.5	Schedule	0236	1424			
Analyses	0300	0400	0500	0900	1100	1200	1500	1800	2100	2300
Forecasts (24hr)	0524	0800	1000	1300	1736	2200				

The charts cover the North Atlantic, Europe and the Mediterranean and there is a wealth of other Met charts on the broadcast.

Quickborn/Pinneberg (D) - (Fax)

Frequencies	3855	7880	13882.5	Schedule	1111		
Analyses	0430	0525	0743	1050	1600	1800	2200
Forecasts	24/30/72/96-hour						
	0512(30) 0717(30) 0730(48) 0804(72) 0817(96) 1834(24)						
	Repeat of 0730 and 0804 transmission 1847(48) 1900(72)						

Rome (I) - (Fax)

Frequencies	4777.5	8146.6	13597.5

Status of broadcast unknown

Quickborn/Pinneberg (D) - (Radio-telex)

The Deutscher Wetterdienst maintains two radio-telex broadcasts for shipping. Both broadcasts are on 24 hours a day and the contents include warnings, forecast bulletins including detailed wind forecasts at grid points. Observations in the standard WMO code form are also available for the main synoptic hours. The forecasts are for the waters around north west Europe and the Mediterranean. Many of the bulletins are in English. The full schedule is available on the Internet at: www.dwd.de/services/gfsf/e_telexpln.html.

NAVTEX (SEE PAGE 5)

Message category codes:

A – Navigational warning
B – Gale warning
C – Ice report
D – Search and Rescue information
E – Weather forecast
F – Pilot service message
G – DECCA messages
H – LORAN messages
I – OMEGA messages
J – SATNAV messages
K – Other electronic navaid messages
L – Navigational warnings - additional to A
Z – No messages on hand

Times of NAVTEX weather bulletins

Gale warnings are broadcast by NAVTEX on receipt. Full weather bulletins (A) including 24-hour forecasts for sea areas within 200 to 300 miles of the transmitting station, gale warnings (B) and extended outlooks (C) are broadcast on 518kHz at the following times:

Transmitting station	Times GMT			
Metarea I	(A)		(B) 4-hourly from:b	(C)
Bodo (B), Norway	0010	1210	0010	
Cullercoats (G), UK	0900	2100	0100	0100
Stockholm (Bjuroklubb)(H), Sweden	0910	2110	0110	
Stockholm (Gislovshammar)(J), Sweden	0930	2130	0130	
Stockholm (Grimeton)(D)	0830	2030	0030	
Rogaland (L), Norway	0150	1350	0150	
Portpatrick (O), UK	0620	1820	0220	0220
Niton (E), UK	0840	2040	0040	2300
Malin Head (Q), Rep of Ireland	1040	2240	0240	
Valentia (W), Rep of Ireland	0740	1940	0340	
Ostend (T), Belgium	0710	1910	0310	
Tallinn (U), Estonia	0720	1920	0320	
Vardo (V), Norway	1130	2330	0330	
Metarea II				
Corsen (A), France	0000	1200	0000	
Coruña (D), Spain	0030	1230	0030	
Monsanto (R), Portugal	0905	2105		
Horta (F), Azores			0050	
La Garde (W), France (Med coast)	1140	2340	0340	
Tarifa (G) Spain	0900	2100		
Valencia (X) Spain	0750	1950		
Metarea III				
Split (Q)	4 hourly from 0240		0240	
Cyprus (M)	4-hourly from 0200		0200	
Iraklion (H), Greece	4-hourly from 0110		0110	
Limnos (L), Greece	4-hourly from 0150		0150	
Samsun (E), Turkey	4-hourly from 0030		0030	
Kerkyra (K) Greece	4-hourly from 0140		0140	
Malta (O)	0620	1820		

NATIONAL NAVTEX SERVICE

A national NAVTEX service is now being disseminated on 490kHz. On this service, the forecast for the relevant areas of the 16-area inshore waters forecast is broadcast twice a day (all times are UTC).

Cullercoats [U]	Niton [I]	Portpatrick [C]
0720 1920	0520 1720	0820 2020

The bulletins include 24-hour **forecasts** and 24-hour outlooks (including a forecast of the sea state), and a **three-day national outlook**. Strong-wind warnings are also broadcast on the national NAVTEX transmissions, these being broadcast on receipt and then repeated in the routine four-hourly broadcast slots until the warning expires. The MCA advises that further information is planned to be broadcast on the national NAVTEX service.

FORECASTS FOR EASTERN NORTH ATLANTIC

Radio France Internationale (RFI) provides a full weather bulletin including a 36-hour forecast in French for the Eastern North Atlantic at 1140 GMT daily. The broadcast frequencies are:

6175 kHz for reception in Europe, 11845 for reception in the Mediterranean, 13640, 15300, 15515, 17575kHz for reception in the Atlantic

Areas covered are shown on the chart on page 53

Forecasts for Metareas I and II are also available via the Inmarsat SafetyNET™ service (see page 5 for times of transmission).

SCHEDULE OF WEATHER BULLETINS

available to yachtsmen in West European waters, transmitted in plain language by radio telephony.

In the following schedule, the references to Areas are those indicated on the chart of the appropriate country which follow the schedule. All times are GMT unless indicated otherwise.

The key to the abbreviations used is as follows:

A Full weather bulletin and forecast.

B Strong wind and storm warnings or gale warnings.

C Forecast for coastal waters only.

D Fog forecast.

1 Time depending on transmitter used.

2 Sea area boundaries as for United Kingdom.

3 Gale warning summaries for appropriate sea areas are broadcast at 0303, 0903, 1503, 2103.

4 See chart for appropriate country.

5 1 April to 30 September only.

6 1 May to 31 August only.

7 Strong wind and gale warning summaries for local area only are broadcast at 0645, 1345, 1845, 2245, GMT. Strong wind warnings issued for Force 7, or gusts to Force 8.

8 Clock times.

9 H + 03, H + 33 until period of validity then change to time given in brackets.

† Retransmission of earlier broadcast.

* See also pages 4 to 11.

Notes

In addition to the scheduled services shown, a number of stations broadcast strong wind/gale warnings on receipt and at the end of the next silence period after receipt.

If it is necessary to convert from kHz into metres divide kHz into 300,000 e.g:

200kHz = 300,000 ÷ 200 = 1500 metres

Some broadcasts give wind speed in metres per second. For conversion to knots multiplication by 2 is near enough.

1 knot = 0.515m/sec.   1m/sec = 1.94 knots.

United Kingdom

Forecasts and warnings are broadcast via the HM Coastguard MRCC and MRSC stations. The tables below give the schedule for both the MF and VHF network. All times are GMT.

MF stations (Initial call on 2182 kHz)

Station	Frequency	Shipping Forecast	Gale, Storm, Strong Wind Warnings[†]	Areas
Shetland	1770kHz	0905, 2150	0105, 0505, 0905, 1305, 1705, 2105	Faeroes, Fair Isle, Viking
Aberdeen	226kHz	0720, 1920	0320, 0720, 1120, 1520, 1920, 2305	Fair Isle, Cromarty, Forth, Forties
Humber	2226kHz	0740, 1940	0340, 0740, 1140, 1540, 1940, 2340	Tyne, Dogger, German Bight, Humber
Yarmouth	1869kHz	0840, 2040	0040, 0440, 0840, 1240, 1640, 2040	Humber, Thames
Solent	1641kHz	0840, 2040	0040, 0440, 0840, 1240, 1640, 2040	Portland, Wight
Falmouth	2226kHz	0940, 2140	0140, 0540, 0940, 1340, 1740, 2140	Plymouth, Lundy, Fastnet, Sole
Milford Haven	1767kHz	0735, 1935	0335, 0735, 1135, 1535, 1935, 2335	Lundy, Irish Sea, Fastnet
Holyhead	1880kHz	0635, 1835	0235, 0635, 1035, 1435, 1835, 2235	Irish Sea
Clyde	1883kHz	0820, 2020	0020, 0420, 0820, 1220, 1620, 2020	Bailey, Hebrides, Rockall, Malin
Stornoway	1743kHz	0910, 2110	0110, 0510, 0910, 1310, 1710, 2110	Fair Isle, Faeroes, Hebrides, Bailey, Malin, Rockall

[†] Note that Gale, Storm or Strong Wind Warnings are broadcast on receipt from the Met Office and repeated in the four-hourly slots indicated while the warning is in force. Strong wind warnings are only broadcast if the warning indicates a significant change to the inshore waters forecast which could result in problems for small craft.

VHF Service (Initial call on Ch16 and then broadcast on either Ch10 or Ch73)

Station	Shipping forecast	Local Inshore Waters Forecast Gale, Storm & Strong Wind Warnings†	Areas
Shetland	0905, 2105	0105, 0505, 0905, 1305, 1705, 2105	Faeroes, Fair Isle, Viking
Aberdeen	0720, 1920	0320, 0720, 1120, 1520, 1920, 2305	Fair Isle, Cromarty, Forth, Forties
Forth	1005, 2205	0205, 0605, 1005, 1405, 1805, 2205	Forth, Tyne, Dogger, Forties
Humber	0740, 1940	0340, 0740, 1140, 1540, 1940, 2340	Tyne, Dogger, Humber
Yarmouth	0840, 2040	0040, 0440, 0840, 1240, 1640, 2040	Humber, Thames
Thames	0810, 2010	0010, 0410, 0810, 1210, 1610, 2010	Thames, Dover
Dover	0905, 2105	0105, 0505, 0905, 1305, 1705, 2105	Thames, Dover, Wight
Solent	0840, 2040	0040, 0440, 0840, 1240, 1640, 2040	Portland, Wight
Portland	1020, 2220	0220, 0620, 1020, 1420, 1820, 2220	Plymouth, Portland, Wight
Brixham	0850, 2050	0050, 0450, 0850, 1250, 1650, 2050	Plymouth, Portland
Falmouth	0940, 2140	0140, 0540, 0940, 1340, 1740, 2140	Plymouth, Lundy, Fastnet, Sole
Swansea	0805, 2005	0005, 0405, 0805, 1205, 1605, 2005	Lundy, Irish Sea, Fastnet
Milford Haven	0735, 1935	0335, 0735, 1135, 1535, 1935, 2335	Lundy, Irish Sea, Fastnet
Holyhead	0635, 1835	0235, 0635, 1035, 1435, 1835, 2235	Irish Sea
Liverpool	1010, 2210	0210, 0610, 1010, 1410, 1810, 2210	Irish Sea, Malin
Belfast	0705, 1905	0305, 0705, 1105, 1505, 1905, 2305	Irish Sea, Malin
Clyde	0820, 2020	0020, 0420, 0820, 1220, 1620, 2020	Malin, Hebrides
Oban	0640, 1840	0240, 0640, 1040, 1440, 1840, 2240	Malin, Hebrides
Stornoway	0910, 2110	0110, 0510, 0910, 1310, 1710, 2110	Fair Isle, Malin, Hebrides, Rockall, Bailey, Faeroes

† Note that Gale, Storm or Strong Wind Warnings are broadcast on receipt from the Met Office and repeated in the four-hourly slots indicated while the warning is in force. Strong wind warnings are only broadcast if the warning indicates a significant change to the inshore waters forecast which could result in problems for small craft.

Station	Channel	Frequency kHz	Times of broadcast GMT	Sea areas[4]	Information given	Language
Jersey	25,82	1659	0645[8] 0745[8] 0845[6,8] 1245 1845 2245	Waters around Channel Isles, south of 50°N and east of 3°W	A[7]	English
BBC Radio 4[8]		198, MW and FM	0048 0536	All U.K. sea areas	A	English
		198, and MW	1201 1754	All U.K. sea areas	A	English
		198, MW and FM	0053 0540	U.K. inshore waters	C	English
BBC Radio Guernsey		1116 93.2MHz	0807 1235 (Mon-Fri) 0810 Sat, Sun	Waters around Guernsey	C	English
BBC Radio Jersey		1026 88.8MHz	0635 0810 1835 (Mon-Fri) 0735 Sat, Sun	Waters around Jersey	C	English
RAF Volmet		5450 11253	continuous (see page 5)			
London Volmet (main)		135.375MHz	continuous			
London Volmet (north)		126.600MHz	continuous			
Scottish Volmet		125.725MHz	continuous			

Belgium

Station	Channel	Frequency kHz	Times of broadcast GMT	Sea areas[4]	Information given	Language
Ostend	27	2761	0820 1720	Dover, Thames	A	English & Dutch

Croatia

Station	Channel	Frequency kHz	Times of broadcast GMT	Sea areas[4]	Information given	Language
Dubrovnik	04, 07		0625 1320 2120	Adriatic	A	National & English
Split	07, 21 28		0545 1245 1945	Adriatic	A	National & English
Rijeka	24		0535 1435 1935	Adriatic	A	National & English
	67, 69, 73		continuous broadcast	Adriatic	C	National & English

Cyprus

Station	Channel	Frequency kHz	Times of broadcast GMT	Sea areas[4]	Information given	Language
		2700	0200 0600 0000 1400 1800 2200	Eastern Mediteranean	A	English
BFBS		89.7MHz 92.1 99.6	0635 (Mon-Sat) 0731 1014 1310 (Mon-Fri) 0959 (Sun)		C	English

Station	Channel	Frequency kHz	Times of broadcast GMT	Sea areas[4]	Information given	Language
Denmark						
Lyngby		1704 1734 1758 2586	on receipt	North Sea and Baltic	B	English
Danmarks Radio[8]		243 1062 2145	0445 0745 1045 1645	North Sea and Baltic	A	Danish
Estonia						
Tallinn		3310	4 hourly from 0233	Baltic	B	English & Estonian
Finland						
Turku	01, 02, 03 04, 05, 23 24, 25, 26 27, 28, 84 85, 86, 88	1719 2810	0733 1933	Gulf of Finland, Bothnia and North Baltic	A	English
France						
France Inter[8]		162	2003	All sea areas except southern Mediterranean	A	French
France Bleu			0640			
Ajaccio, Brest		1404	0640	All sea areas except southern Mediterranean		
Bastia, Bayonne		1494				
Bordeaux		1206				
Lille		1377				
Limoges		792				
Marseille		1242				
Nice		1557				
Paris		864				
Rennes		711				
Toulouse		945				

French Maritime Rescue Co-ordination Centres (CROSS) broadcast general weather bulletins and warnings of strong winds and visibility less than two miles (Bulletins Meteorologique Speciaux (BMS)) as follows

Station	Channel	Time	Sea Areas	Information	Language
Joborg	80	H+20,H+50	Manche Ouest & Est	B	French
Corsen	79	3-hourly at H+50 from 0850 in summer 0950 in winter	Manche Ouest, Ouest Bretagne, Nord Gascogne	A	French
	79	H+10, H+40		B	French

CROSS broadcast bulletins for coastal waters as follows. Associated BMS are mostly for the zones of responsibility defined on page 56. *indicates 1 May to 30 September only.

CROSS	Transmitter	Channel	Time	Coastal Zone
Griz-Nez	Dunkirk	79	0720 1603 1920	Dunkirk to Somme
	Griz-Nez	79	0710 1545 1910	
Griz-Nez	Ailly	79	0703 1533 1903	Somme to La Hague
Jobourg	Antifer	80	0803 1633 2003	
	Port en Bessin	80	0745 1615 1945	
	Jobourg	80	0733 1603 1933	
Joborg	Joborg	80	0715 1545 1915	la Hague to Penmarc'h
	Granville	80	0703 1533 1903	
	Raz	79	0445 0703 1103* 1533 1903	
	Stiff	79	0503 0715 1115* 1545 1915	
	Batz	79	0515 0733 1133* 1603 1933	
	Bodic	79	0533 0745 1145* 1615 1945	
	Frehel	79	0545 0803 1203* 1633 2003	
Etel	Penmarc'h	80	0703 1533 1903	Penmarc'h to l'Aiguillon
	Groix	80	0715 1545 1915	
	Belle Ile	80	0733 1603 1933	
	St Nazaire	80	0745 1615 1945	
	Yeu	80	0803 1633 2003	
	Sables d'Olonne	80	0815 1645 2015	
Etel	Chassiron	79	0703 1533 1903	l'Aiguillon to Spain
	Soulac	79	0715 1545 1915	
	Cap-Ferret	79	0733 1603 1933	
	Contis	79	0745 1615 1945	
	Biarritz	79	0803 1633 2003	
La Garde	Néoulos	79	0703 1233 1903	Spain to Port-Camargue
	Agde	79	0715 1245 1915	
La Garde	Planier	80	0733 1303 1933	Port-Camargue to St Raphael
	Mont Coudon	80	0745 1315 1945	
La Garde	Pic de l'Ours	80	0803 1333 2003	St Raphael to Menton
La Garde	Ersa	79	0733 1233 1933	Corsican coast
	Serra de Pigno	79	0745 1245 1945	
	Conca	79	0803 1303 2003	
	Serragia	79	0815 1315 2015	
	Punta	79	0833 1333 2033	
	Piana	79	0845 1345 2045	

Station	Channel	Frequency kHz	Times of broadcast GMT	Sea areas[4]	Information given	Language

Germany

Station	Channel	Frequency kHz	Times of broadcast GMT	Sea areas[4]	Information given	Language
Norddeutscher Rundfunk[8]		702 972 and FM	0005 0830 2200	German Bight, SW and Central North Sea, West and mid Baltic	A	German
Radio Bremen		936 6190 and FM	0928 2300	German Bight, Southern North Sea, and West Baltic	C A	German German
Deutschlandfunk[8]		1269	0105 0640 1105	East North Sea, West and mid Baltic	A	German
Norddeich	28		0700[8] 1800[8]	Southern North Sea	A	German
Helgoland	27					
Elbe-Weser	24					
Eider Stedt	25					
Nordfriesland	26					
Flensburg	25		0630[8] 1730[8]	South Baltic	A	German
Kiel	26					
Lübek	27					
Rostock	25					
Fischland	23					
Arkona	01					
Rügen	05					

Gibraltar

Station	Channel	Frequency kHz	Times of broadcast GMT	Sea areas[4]	Information given	Language
		1458 91.3,92.6 100.5MHz	0630 (ex Sun) 0730, 0830,1130 1740 (Mon-Fri)	Sailing forecast up to 50M from Gibraltar	A	English

Greece

Station	Channel	Frequency kHz	Times of broadcast GMT	Sea areas[4]	Information given	Language
Athinai		2590	0703 0933 1503 2103	Greek waters	A	Greek & English
Hellenic Radio/TV		729 927 1044 1494 1512 1602	0430 1330	All areas All areas	A A	Greek & English Greek
Heraklion Radio		2799	0703 0903 1533 2133	Greek waters	B	Greek & English
Kerkyra Radio		2830	0703 0903 1533 2133	Greek waters	A	Greek & English
Limnos Radio		2730	0703 0903 1533 2133	Greek waters	A	Greek & English

Station	Channel	Frequency kHz	Times of broadcast GMT	Sea areas[4]	Information given	Language
Ireland[8]						
Radio Eireann		567 and FM	0602 1253 1823 1824 (Sat & Sun) 2355 (Mon-Fri only)	Irish waters within 30 miles of coast and Irish Sea	C	English
Wicklow Head	87		3-hourly from 0103	Irish coastal waters	C	English
Malin Head	23					
Cork	26					
Shannon	28					
Dublin	83					
Valentia	24			Fastnet, Shannon	A	English
Valentia, MRCS		1752	0833 2033	Fastnet, Shannon	A	English
Shannon Volmet		3413 5505 8957 13264	night continuous (see page 5) day			
Dublin Volmet		127.0MHz	continuous			
Italy						
Ancona	25	2656	0135 0735 1335 1935	Areas 12, 13	A	Italian & English
Augusta	26	2628	0135 0735 1335 1935	Areas 8, 9	A	Italian & English
Bari	26, 27	2579	0135 0735 1335 1935	Areas 8, 9, 10, 11	A	Italian & English
Cagliari	25, 26, 27	2680	0135 0735 1335 1935	Areas 3, 4, 6	A	Italian & English
Civitavecchia	27	1888	0135 0735 1335 1935	Areas 5, 6	A	Italian & English
Crotone	25	2663	0135 0735 1335 1935	Areas 9,10	A	Italian & English
Genova	25, 27	2722	0135 0735 1335 1935	Areas 1, 2, 5	A	Italian & English
Lampedusa	26	1876	0135 0735 1335 1935	Area 4, 7 and Libyan Sea	A	Italian & English
Livorno	26, 84	2591	0135 0735 1335 1935	Areas 1, 5, 6	A	Italian & English
Mazara del Vallo	25	2600	0135 0735 1335 1935	Area 8	A	Italian & English

Station	Channel	Frequency kHz	Times of broadcast GMT	Sea areas[4]	Information given	Language
Messina	25	2789	0135 0735 335 1935	Areas 7, 9, 10	A	Italian & English
Napoli	25, 27	2632	0135 0735 1335 1935	Areas 6, 7	A	Italian & English
Palermo	27	1852	0135 0735 1335 1935	Areas 7, 8	A	Italian & English
Port Torres	26	2719	0135 0735 1335 1935	Areas 2, 3, 6	A	Italian & English
Radio Italia[8] (Radiodue)		846 936 1035 1116 1188 1314 1431 1449	0621 1432 2223	All Italian sea areas	A	Italian
Roma	25		0135 0735 1335 1935	Areas 5, 6	A	Italian & English
S. Benedetto del Tronto		1855	0135 0735 1335 1935	Area 12	A	Italian & English
Trieste	25	2624	0135 0735 1335 1935	Areas 12, 13	A	Italian & English

A contnouous broadcast of weather information in Italian and English is available on Channel 67 for areas local to the transmitter.

Malta

Malta	04	2625	0603 1003 1603 2103	Maltese coastal waters up to 50 miles offshore	C	English

Monaco

Monaco		8728 8806	0715 1830	West Med	A	French & English
Monaco	23	continuous broadcast (changed 3 times per day)		La Ciotat to San Remo	A	French & English
Monaco[8]	20	4363.6	0903 1403 1915	Lion, Provence, Genes, Corse, Ouest Sardaigne Nord Baleares (Mon - Fri)	A	French & English
Riviera Radio[8]		106.3 106.5MHz	0715 0815 1240 1710 1915	La Ciotat to Menton	C	English

Montenegro

Bar	24	1720	0850 1420 2050	Adriatic	A	National & English

Station	Channel	Frequency kHz	Times of broadcast GMT	Sea areas[4]	Information given	Language
Netherlands						
Coastguard		3673	0940 2140	North Sea and Netherlands coastal waters	A	Dutch & English
	23 83		0805 1305 2305	Netherlands coastal waters	C	Dutch
Amsterdam Volmet		126.2MHz	continuous (see page 5)			
Norway						
Rogaland Radio		6507 8749 13158	2305 1205 2305 1205	Coastal waters of South Norway and North Sea	A	Norwegian & English
Poland						
Gdynia	24, 25, 26	1692 2726	0135 0735 1335 1935	Baltic	A	Polish & English
Portugal						
CTN		2657	0735 2335	Coastal waters of Portugal	C	Portuguese & English
Sagres		2567	0835 2035	Coastal waters of Portugal	C	Portuguese & English
(Portuguese Radio) Lisboa Faro Porto		666 720 1287	1100[8]	Portuguese coastal waters	C	Portuguese
Spain						
Cabo de Penas FitzRoy		1677 1764 1698	0803 1703 0803 1703 0833 1733	Gran Sol, Vizcaya Cantabrico FitzRoy	A	Spanish La Coruna
Machichaco		1707	0903 1733			
Tarifa		1704	0803 1703	San Vincente	A	Spanish
Chipiona		1656	0833 1733	Cadiz, Alboran		
Cabo de Gata		1767	0833 1733	Palos, Leon, Baleares, Argelia	A	Spanish
Palma (Mallorca)		1755	0803 1703	Palos, Leon, Baleares, Argelia	A	Spanish
Bilbao	26		0940 1140 2140	Spanish coastal waters	C	Spanish & English
Bilbao MRCC	11		4 hourly from 0033		C	Spanish & English
Santander	24		0940 1140 2140		C	Spanish & English
Santander MRSC	11		4 hourly from 0245			

Station	Channel	Frequency kHz	Times of broadcast GMT	Sea areas[4]	Information given	Language
Coruña	02, 26		0950 1150 2150		A	
Coruña MRSC	12, 13, 14		4 hourly from 0005		A	
Finisterre	01, 22		4 hourly from 0233		A	
Cadiz	26		0940 1140 2140		A	
Malaga	26, 81		0940 1140 2140		A	
Tarifa MRCC	10, 74		Even H+15		A	
Cabo Gata	27		0940 1140 2140	Spanish Coastal Waters	A	Spanish and English
Cartagena	04		0940 1140 2140		A	
Alicante	04		0940 1140 2140		A	
Almeria MRCC	10, 74		Every H+15		A	
Valencia MRCC	10		Even H+15		A	
Castellon	25		0935 1140 2140		A	
Tarragona MRCC	13		0433 0833 1433 1933		A	
Barcelona	10		0500 0900 1400 1900		A	
MRCC	10, 16		0700 1000 1630 2130		A	
Palma	10		0635 0935 1435 1935		A	
Palma Radio			0920 1120		A	
Mallorca	20				A	
Ibiza	03				A	
Menorca	85				A	
Palamos Radio	13		0630 1333 1833		A	

Sweden

Station	Channel	Frequency kHz	Times of broadcast GMT	Sea areas[4]	Information given	Language
Karlskrona		2789	0954 2154	South & Central Baltic	A	Swedish & English
Stockholm	23, 24	1674	0733 1933	Baltic	A	Swedish & English
	25, 26	1710				
	27, 28	1779				
	64, 66	1797				
	81, 84	2733				
Tingstade		2768	1006 2206	South & Central Baltic	A	Swedish & English
Sveriges Radio		1179 FM	0455 1455 0655 1200 1455 2050	Eastern North Sea and Baltic	A	

Turkey[8]

Station	Channel	Frequency kHz	Times of broadcast GMT	Sea areas[4]	Information given	Language
Samsun		3636 6965	0750 1950	Black Sea	C	Turkish & English

Canaries

Station	Channel	Frequency kHz	Times of broadcast GMT	Sea areas[4]	Information given	Language
Arrecife	25		0903 1803		C	Spanish & English
Las Palmas		518	0920 1320 1720		C	Spanish & English

CHARTS OF SEA AREAS

UNITED KINGDOM

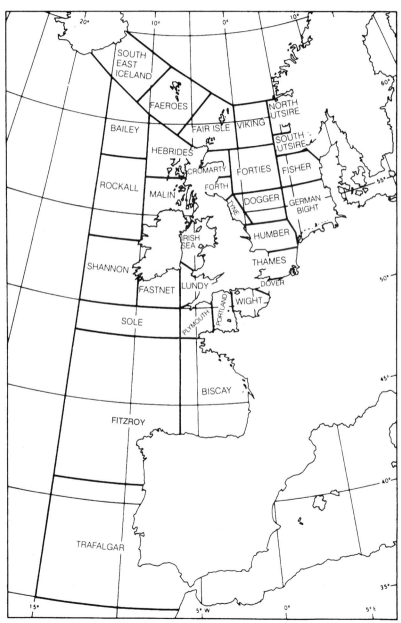

NORTH SEA COMMON AREAS

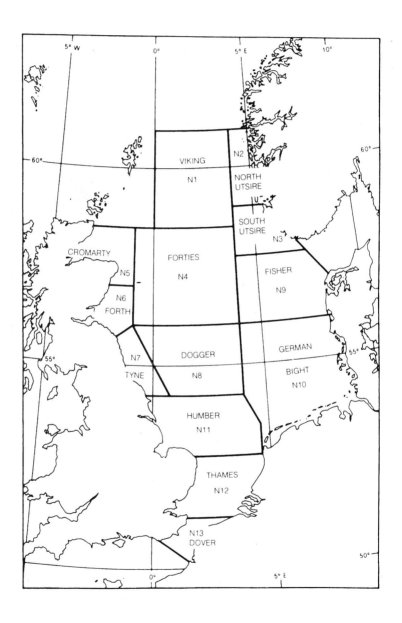

BALTIC COMMON AREAS

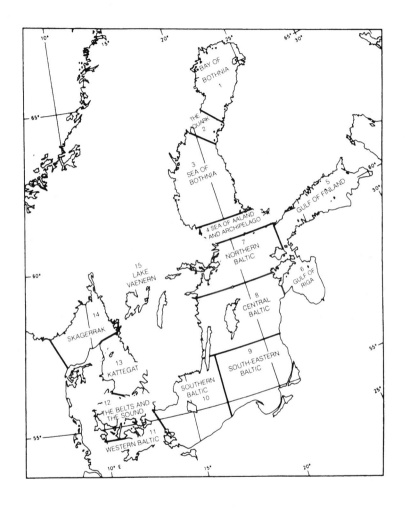

FRANCE

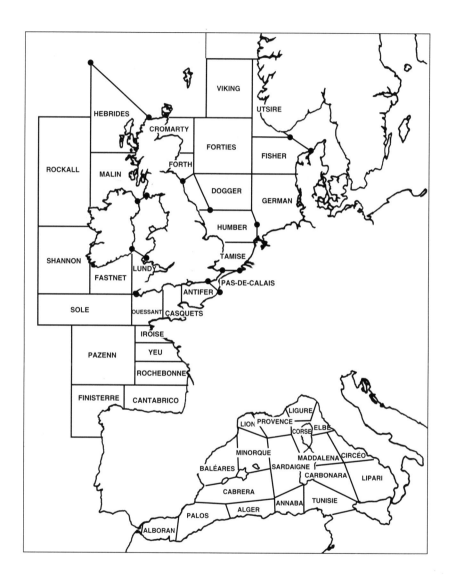

FRANCE

Sea areas used by Radio France International (see page 42)

FRANCE

CROSS areas of responsibility (see page 43)

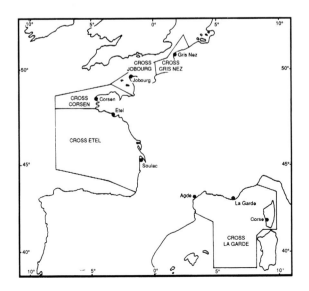

FRANCE / SPAIN / PORTUGAL

Metarea II sea areas used in GMDSS and Navtex (See pages 5 & 37)

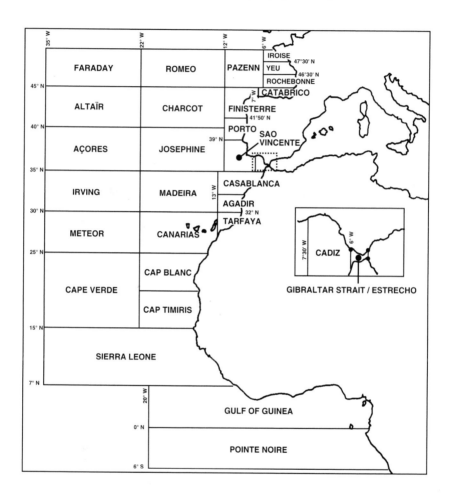

ITALY

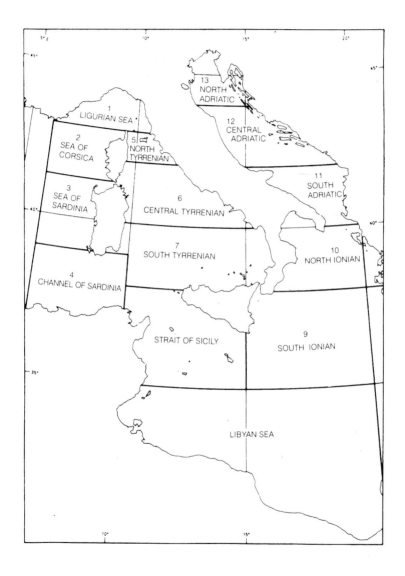

GREECE

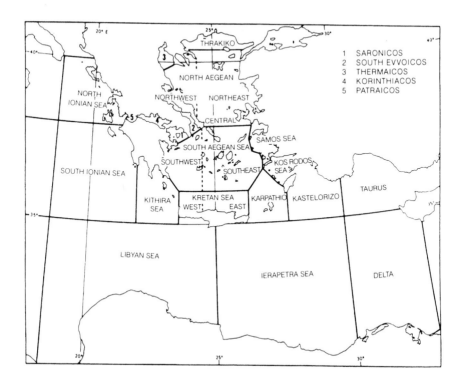

1 SARONICOS
2 SOUTH EVVOICOS
3 THERMAICOS
4 KORINTHIACOS
5 PATRAICOS

SPAIN

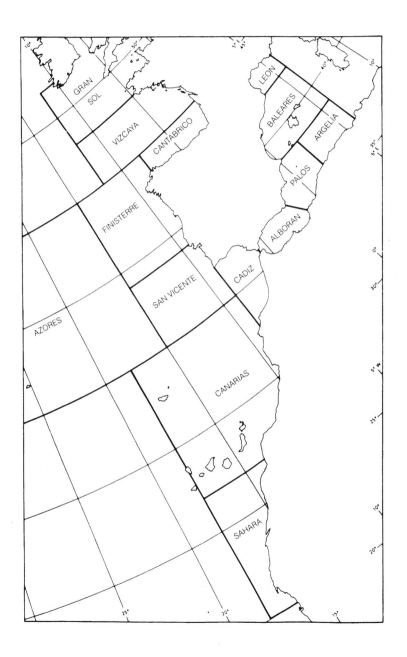

INTERNATIONAL WEATHER VOCABULARY

ENGLISH	DANISH	DUTCH	FRENCH	GERMAN	ITALIAN	SPANISH
A Amendment	Aendring	Verandering	Changement Amendement	Änderung	Correzione	Enmienda Rectification
Area	Farvand	Gebied	Zone	Gebiet	Area	Zona
B Backing	Venstredrejende	Krimpend	Recul du vent	Rückdrehend	Rotazione a Sinistra Rotazione Antioraria	Rolada a la Izquierda
Beaufort Wind Scale	Beaufort's Vindskala	Beaufortschaal voor Windkracht	Echelle de Beaufort	Beaufortskala	Scala di Beaufort	Escala Beaufort
C Calm	Vindstille	Windstilte	Calme	Windstille	Calmo	Calma
Centre	Centrum Center	Centrum	Centre	Zentrum	Centro	Centro
Choppy	Skiftende	Woelig	Hachée	Kabbelige	Mosso	Agitado
Clouds	Skyer	Wolken	Nuages	Wolken	Nubi	Nubes
Clouds (broken)	Skyet	Gebroken	Nuages Fragmentés Troué	Bewölkung	Nubirotte	Quebrado, Nubes Fragmentadas
Cloudy	Overskyet	Bewolkt	Nuageux	Bewölkt	Nuvoloso	Nublado, Nuboso
Coast	Kyst	Kust	Côte	Küste	Costa	Costa
Coastal	Kyst-	Kust-	Littoral	An der Küste	Costiero	Costero
Cold	Kold	Koud	Froid	Kalt	Freddo	Frio
Cyclonic	Cyklonisk	Cycloonachtig, Cyclonisch	Cyclonique	Zyklonisch	Ciclonico	Ciclonica
D Dawn	Daggry	Dageraad Morgenschemering	Aube, au point du jour	Morgendämmerung	Alba	Alba
Decrease (Wind)	Aftagen	Afnemen	Affaiblissement, Diminution	Abnahme	Caduto, Diminuzione	Disminución
Deep	Dyb	Diep	Profond	Tief	Profondo	Profundo
Deepening	Uddybende	Verdiepend	Creusement	Vertiefung	Approfondimento	Ahondamiento
Dense	Taet, Tyk	Dicht	Dense	Dicht	Denso	Denso
Depression (Low)	Lavtryk	Depressie	Dépression	Tief	Depressione	Depresión
Direction	Retning	Richting	Direction	Richtung	Direzione	Dirreción
Dispersing	Som spreder sig	Verstrooiend	Se dispersant, se dissipant	Zerstreuung	Dispersione	Disipación
Drizzle	Finregn	Motregen	Bruine	Sprühregen	Spruzzatore, Pioviggne	Lloviznaa
Dusk	Tusmørke	Avondschemering	Brune, crépuscule du soir	Abenddämmerung	Crepusculo Tramontana	Crepúsculo

ENGLISH	DANISH	DUTCH	FRENCH	GERMAN	ITALIAN	SPANISH
E East	Øst	Oosten	Est	Ost	Est Levante	Este
Extending	Udstraekkende	Uitstrekkend	Extension	Ausbreitend	Estendo	Extension
Extensive (or Widespread)	Udstrackt	Uitgestrekt	Extendue	Verbreitet	Esteso	General
F Falling	Faldende	Dalend, Vallend	En Baisse	Fallend	In diminuzione	En disminucion
Filling	Udfyldende	(Op) Vullend	Comblement	Auffüllend	Riempimento Colmamento	Relleno
Fine (or Fair)	Smukt, (Klart)	Mooi	Clair, Beau	Schönwetter	Sereno, bello	Sereno
Fog	Taage	Mist	Brouillard	Nebel	Nebbia	Niebla
Fog bank	Taage Banke	Mist Bank	Banc de Brouillard	Nebelbank	Banco di Nebbia	Banco de Niebla
Forecast	Vejrforudsigelse	Verwachting	Prévision	Vorhersage	Previsione	Previsión
Formation	Formation	Formatie	Formation	Bildung	Formazione	Formación
Forming	Danne (dannende)	Vorming	Developpent,	Formend,	Formando se formant	Formante bildend
Frequent	Hyppig	Veelvuldig	Fréquent	Häufig	Frequente	Frecuenta
Fresh	Frisk	Fris	Fraiche, frais	Frisch	Fresco	Fresco
Front	Front	Front	Front	Front	Fronte	Frente
Front (passage of)	Front passage	Front Passage	Passage d'un Front	Frontdurch- gang	Passaggio di un Fronte	Paso de un Frente
Frost	Frost	Vorst	Gelée	Frost	Brina	Escarcha
G Gale	Stormende Kuling, Hard Kuling	Stormachtig	Coup de Vent	Stürmischer wind	Burrasca	Viento Duro
Cones (Gale)	Oje	Kegel	Cône	Sturmekegel	Sintoma	Cona
Gale warning	Stormvarsel	Stormwaarsch- uwing	Avis de coup de Vent	Sturmwarnung	Avviso di Burrasca	Aviso de Temporal
Good	God	Goed	Bon	Gut	Buono	Bueono
Gust	Vinstød, Vindkast	Windstoot	Rafale	Windstoss	Colpo di Vento, Raffica	Ráfaga, Racha
Gusty	Stormfuld, Byget	Buiig	(Vent) à Rafales	Böig	Con Raffiche	en Räfagas en Rachas
H Hail	Hagl	Hagel	Grêle	Hagel	Grandine	Granizo
Haze	Dls	Nevel	Brume Sèche	Dunst (Trockener)	Caligine	Calina
Hazy	Diset	Nevelig	Brumeux	Diesig	Caliginoso	Calinoso
Heavy	Svaer, Kraftig	Zwaar	Abondant, Violent	Ergiebig, Schwer	Pesante, Violento	Abunante, Violento
High (Anticyclone)	Anticyklon, Højtryk	Hogedruk- gebeid	Anticyclone	Antizyklone Hockdruck- gebiet	Anticiclone	Anticiclón

ENGLISH	DANISH	DUTCH	FRENCH	GERMAN	ITALIAN	SPANISH
Hurricane	Orkan	Orkaan	Ouragan	Orkan (auuserhalb der Tropen), Hurrikan	Uragano	Huracán
I Increasing	Tiltagende, øgende	Toenemend	Augmentant	Zunehmend	In Auhmento	Aumentar
Intermittent	Intermitternde, Tiltider, Tidvis	Afwisselend	Intermittent	Zeitweilig	Intermittente	Intermitente
Isobar	Isobar	Isobar	Isobare	Isobare	Isobara	Isobara
Isolated	Isolere, Enkelte	Verspreid	Isolé	Einzelne	Isolato	Aislado
L Latitude	Bredde	Breedte	Latitude	Breite	Latitudine	Latitud
Light, slight	Tynd, let	Licht, Gering, Zwak	Faible	Schwach	Leggero, Debole	Ligero, Dehil
Lightning	Lyn	Bliksem	Eclair Foudre	Blitz	Lampo	Recámpago
Line squall	Bygelinie	Buienlijn	Ligne de Grain	Böenfront	Linea di Groppo	Linea de Turbonada
Local	Lokal	Plaatselijk	Locale	Örtlich, Lokal	Locale	Local
Longtitude	Laengde	Lengte	Longitude	Länge	Longitudine	Longitud
M Meridian	Meridian	Meridiaan	Méridien	Meridian Langenkreis	Meridiano	Meridiano
Mist	Let Tåge, Tågedis	Nevel	Brume Légère	Dunst (Feuchter)	Foschia, Brumo	Neblina
Misty	Taget, Diset	Nevelig	Brumeux	Dunstig, Diesig	Brumoso,	Fosco Brumoso
Moderate	Middlemadig, Moderat	Matig, Gematigd	Modéré	Mässig	Moderato	Moderado
Moderating	Beherske	Matigend, Afnemend	Se Modérant Se Calmant	Abschwäch-end Abnehmend	Medianente, Calmante	Medianente
Morning (in the)	Om Formiddagen Om Morgenen	Morgen, Voormiddag	Le Matin	Morgens	Al Mattino, Par il Mattino	Por la Manana
Moving	Bevaegende	Bewegend	Se Déplaçant	Ziehend	In Movimiento, Si Muove	Movimiento
N North	Nord	Noorden	Nord	Nord	Settentrionale, Nord	Septentrional Boreal
O Occasional	Af og til, Ti tider	At en toe	Eparses	Teilweise	Occasionale	Occasional
Occlusion	Okklusion	Okklusie	Occlusion	Okklusion	Occlusion	Oclusion
Off-shore wind	Fra land vind	Aflandige wind	Vent de Terre	Ablandiger Wind, Landwind	Vento (Brezza) di Terra	Viento Terral
On-shore wind	I land vind Palånsvind	Wind van zee	Vent de mer Brise de mer	Auflandiger Wind, Seewind	Vento (Brezza) di mare	Viento demar
Overcast	Overtrukket Overskyet	Geheel bewolkt	Couvert	Bedeckt	Coperto	Cubierto

ENGLISH	DANISH	DUTCH	FRENCH	GERMAN	ITALIAN	SPANISH
P Period	Periode	Tijdvak, Periode	Période	Periode	Periodo	Periodo
Period of validity	Glydigheds-periode	Geldigheids-duur	Période de Validité	Gültigkeits-dauer	Periodo di Validità	Periodo de Validez
Poor	Ringe, Sigt	Gering Slecht	Mauvais	Schlecht	Mao, Scarso	Mal
Precipitation	Nedbør	Neerslag	Précipitation	Niederschlag	Precipitazione	Precipitación
Pressure	Tryk	Druk	Pression	Druck	Pressione	Presión
Q Quickly	Kvick, Hurtigt	Zeer Snel	Rapidement	Schnell	Pronto	Pronto
R Rain	Regn	Regen	Pluie	Regen	Pioggia	Pluvial, Lluvia
Continuous (rain)	Uafbrudt redvarende	Onafgebroken	Continue	Anhaltend	Continua	Continuo
Slight (rain)	Let	Licht, Gering	Faible	Leicht	Pioggia debole	Débil Legero
Ridge	Ryg	Rug	Dorsale	Rücken	Promontorio	Dorsal
Rising	Stigning	Rijzend, Stijgend	En Hausse	Steigend	Ascendente	Ascendente
Rough	Oprørt	Guur	Agitée	Stürmisch	Agitato, Grosso	Bravo o alborotado
S Scattered	Spredt, Stro	Verspreide	Sporadiques	Zerstreut	Diffuso	Difuso
Sea	Sø, Hav	Zee	Mer	Meer	Mare	Mar
Sea breeze	Søbrise, Havbris	Zeewind	Brise de Mer	Seebrise	Brezze di mare	Virazón
Shower	Byge	Regenbui	Averse	Regenschauer	Rovescio	Aguacero, Chubasco
Sleet	Slud, sne og regne	Natte sneeuw	Grésil	Schneeregen	Nevischio	Aguanieve
Slowly	Langsomt	Zie Langzaam	Lentement	Langsam	Lentamente	Lentamente
Smooth	Glatte	Vlak	Belle	Glatt	Tranquillo, Calmo	Tranquilo, Calmo
Snow	Sne	Sneeuw	Neige	Schnee	Neve	Neive
South	Syd	Zuiden	Sud	Süd	Meridionale	Sur
Squall	Byge	Windvlaag	Grain	Böe	Tempestra	Turbonada
State of sea	Sø Stat, Søeus Tilstand	Toestand van de zee	État de la mer	Zustand der See	Stato del mare	Estado del mare
Stationary	Stationaer	Stationair	Stationnaire	Stationär	Stazionario	Estacionario
Steadily	Regelmaessig	Geregeld, Regelmatig	Regulièrement	Regelmässig	Constante-mente	Constante-mente
Storm	Uneir	Storm	Tempête	Sturm	Tempesta, Tembrale	Temporal
Strong	Staerk, Kraftig	Sterk, Krachtig	Fort	Stark	Forte	Fuerte
Swell	Dønning	Deining	Houle	Dünung	Onda lunga, Mare lungo	Martendida, Mar de Leva
T Thunder	Torden	Donder	Tonnerre	Donner	Tuono	Tormenta
Thunderstorm	Tordenvejr	Onweer	Orage	Gewitter	Temporale	Trueno
Time	Tid	Tijd	Temps	Zeit	Tempo	Hora
Trough	Udlober, Trug	Trog	Creux	Trog	Saccatura	Vaguada

ENGLISH	DANISH	DUTCH	FRENCH	GERMAN	ITALIAN	SPANISH
V Variable	Foranderlig Variabel	Veranderliik	Variable	Veränderlich	Variabile	Variable
Veering	Drejer til Højre	Ruimend	Virement ou Virage	Rechtsdrehend, Ausschiessen	Rotazione ovaria, Rotazione a destra	Dextrogiro
Visibility	Sigt, Sigtbarhed	Zicht	Visibilité	Sicht	Visibilitá	Visibilidad
W Warm	Varm	Warm	Chaud	Warm	Cáldo	Cálido
Waterspout	Skypumpe	Waterhoos	Trombe Marine	Wasserhose	Tromba Marina	Tromba Marina
Wave formation	Bølgeformation	Golfformatie	Formation des Vagues	Wellenbildung	Formazione di onde	Formación de ondas
Weather	Vejr	Weer	Temps	Wetter	Tempo	Tiempo
Weather conditions	Vejr-Betingelse	Weer-somstandig-heden	Conditions du Temps	Wetter-Verhältnisse	Condizioni Tempo	Condiciones del Tiempo
Weather report	Vejrmelding	Weerbericht	Rapport, Météorol-ogique	Wettermel-dung Wetterbericht	Rapporto, (Bollentino) Meteoroligico	Informe, aviso Boletin Meteorologico
West	Vest	Westen	Ouest	West	Ovest, Ponente	Oeste
Whirlwind	Hvirvelvind	Windhoos	Tourbillon de Vent	Wirbelwind	Turbine	Torbellino
Wind	Vind	Wind	Vent	Wind	Vento	Viento
Wind Force	Vindstyrke	Windkracht	Force du Vent	Windstärke	Forza (Intensita) del Vento	Intensidad Fuerrza del Viento

NUMBERS

One	Een	Een	Un(e)	Eins	Uno	Uno
Two	To	Twee	Deux	Zwei	Due	Dos
Three	Tre	Drie	Trois	Drei	Tre	Tres
Four	Fire	Vier	Quatre	Vier	Quattro	Cuatro
Five	Fem	Vijf	Cinq	Fünf	Cinque	Cinco
Six	Seks	Zes	Six	Sechs	Sei	Seis
Seven	Syv	Zeven	Sept	Sieben	Sette	Siete
Eight	Otte	Acht	Huit	Acht	Otto	Ocho
Nine	Ni	Negen	Neuf	Neun	Nove	Nueve
Ten	Ti	Tien	Dix	Zehn	Dieci	Diez

RYA *Membership*

Promoting and Protecting Boating
www.rya.org.uk

The RYA is the national organisation which represents the interests of everyone who goes boating for pleasure.

The greater the membership, the louder our voice when it comes to protecting members' interests.

Apply for membership today, and support the RYA, to help the RYA support you.

nd Protecting Boating

Benefits of Membership

- Access to expert advice on all aspects of boating from legal wrangles to training matters

- Special members' discounts on a range of products and services including boat insurance, books, videos and class certificates

- Free issue of certificates of competence, increasingly asked for by everyone from overseas governments to holiday companies, insurance underwriters to boat hirers

- Access to the wide range of RYA publications, including the quarterly magazine

- Third Party insurance for windsurfing members

- Free Internet access with RYA-Online

- Special discounts on AA membership

- Regular offers in RYA Magazine

- ...and much more

Join online at *www.rya.org.uk* or use the form overleaf.

Visit the website for information, advice, member services and web shop.

If you have previously been a member and know your membership number please enter here ⬚⬚⬚⬚⬚⬚⬚⬚⬚

When completed, please send this form to: RYA RYA House Ensign Way Hamble Southampton SO31 4YA

	Tick box	Cash/Chq.	DD
Family†		£44	£41
Personal		£28	£25
Under 21		£11	£11

Please indicate your main area of interest

- ❑ Yacht Racing
- ❑ Yacht Cruising
- ❑ Dinghy Racing
- ❑ Dinghy Cruising
- ❑ Personal Watercraft
- ❑ Inland Waterways
- ❑ Powerboat Racing
- ❑ Windsurfing
- ❑ Motor Boating
- ❑ Sportsboats and RIBs

These prices are valid until **30.10.03** † Family Membership = 2 adults plus any U21s all living at the same address.

For details of Life Membership and paying over the phone by Credit/Debit card, please call 0845 345 0374/5 or join online at www.rya.org.uk

PLEASE USE BLOCK CAPITALS

Title   Forename   Surname   Date of Birth   Male   Female

1.
2.
3.
4.

Address

Town   County   Postcode

Home Phone No.   Day Phone No.

Facsimile No.   Mobile No.

Email Address

Signature _____   Date _____

RYA

Instructions to your Bank or Building Society to pay by Direct Debit

DIRECT Debit

Please fill in the form and send to:
RYA RYA House Ensign Way Hamble Southampton SO31 4YA Tel: 0845 345 0400

Name and full postal address of your Bank/Building Society

To The Manager	Bank/Building Society
Address	
	Postcode

Name(s) of Account Holder(s)

Bank/Building Society account number

Branch Sort Code

Originator's Identification Number

9	5	5	2	1	3

Reference Number

Instruction to your Bank or Building Society
Please pay Royal Yachting Association Direct Debits from the account detailed in this instruction subject to the safeguards assured by The Direct Debit Guarantee. I understand that this instruction may remain with the Royal Yachting Association and, if so, details will be passed electronically to my Bank/Building Society.

Signature(s)	
Date	

Banks and Building Societies may not accept Direct Debit Instructions for some types of account

---

OR YOU CAN PAY BY CHEQUE

Source Code **077**	Cheque enclosed	£	Made payable to the Royal Yachting Association	**Office use only:** Membership number allocated